Rich Land, Poor Land

BOOKS BY STUART CHASE

The Tragedy of Waste.............*Macmillan*, 1925

Men and Machines................*Macmillan*, 1929

Prosperity, Fact or Myth................*Boni*, 1929

The Nemesis of American Business..*Macmillan*, 1931

Mexico: A Study of Two Americas..*Macmillan*, 1931

A New Deal....................*Macmillan*, 1932

The Economy of Abundance........*Macmillan*, 1934

Government in Business...........*Macmillan*, 1935

Rich Land, Poor Land........*Whittlesey House*, 1936

And in collaboration with

F. J. SCHLINK

Your Money's Worth.............*Macmillan*, 1927

PLATE. I.—GULLY IN STEWART COUNTY, GEORGIA.

RICH LAND
POOR LAND

*A Study of Waste in the Natural Resources
of America*

by

STUART CHASE

New York **WHITTLESEY HOUSE** *London*

M c G R A W - H I L L   B O O K   C O M P A N Y ,   I N C .

THIRTEENTH PRINTING

PUBLISHED BY WHITTLESEY HOUSE
A division of the McGraw-Hill Book Company, Inc.

THE MAPLE PRESS COMPANY, YORK, PA.

Contents

vii

You and your land, your turbulent, seeking land
Where anything can grow.

And they have wasted the pasture and the fresh valley,
Stunk the river, shot the ten thousand sky-darkening pigeon
To build sham castles for imitation Medici
And the rugged sons of the rugged sons of death.

—Stephen Vincent Benét

List of Illustrations

LIST OF ILLUSTRATIONS

MAPS

DIAGRAMS

Rich Land, Poor Land

Chapter I

BETWEEN TWO OCEANS

THE story goes that an old Nebraska farmer was sitting on his porch during a dust storm. Asked what he was watching so intently, he replied: "I'm counting the Kansas farms as they go by."

The people of America have been sitting on their porches watching their continent go by. Kansas farms are good farms, and the North American continent is a good continent. Its beauty, its prodigality in natural resources, its great north and south wedge laid broadside on the temperate zone, make it perhaps the best continent on earth. It is not a little tragic that we should sit on our porches while this great, good continent goes out from under us. It is our homeland. It is where our children must stay. When it is gone—in the sense of a hospitable environment—where shall we live? Many Kansas farms have gone; the whole Dust Bowl is going. Other areas, as we shall see, involving millions of people have lost their resource base of land, water or mineral deposit. We have been called the richest nation ever known, and probably we are—now. But how rich is the most lavish

3

of prodigal sons when the last of his father's bonds has been sold and the proceeds spent?

When I was a boy I used to spend my summers in the White Mountains of New Hampshire, near a mountain named for an Indian chief, Chocorua. The legend was that Chocorua, rather than be captured by the white man, had hurled himself from a great rock near the top of the mountain. The rock was pointed out for all to see. A number of paths led up the mountain, but the one I liked best was the Brook Trail. It began at an abandoned logging camp and wound up a high valley in which a stand of virgin hemlock and spruce by some miracle remained. The trail crossed and recrossed the brook, and in the pools trout flashed. To go through this path was like going through a cathedral; but it smelled sweeter than any cathedral, and no carpet could rival the bed of moss on which one walked. Snowberries grew in the springy litter of brown needles, and checker-berries and Indian slipper plants. Over mossy ledges fringed with maidenhair, icy water trickled on the hottest day. The patches of sunlight on the forest floor, the aromatic scent of spruce and balsam, the feel of the springing earth under one's feet, burned into my youthful memory. It was the most beautiful place I had ever been in, and in retrospect it still seems so. The mountain and the forest stretched down their hands to a sunburned boy and welcomed him. He came to love them and to hate those who harmed them. When on other trails he found tall trees wantonly slaughtered and mountainsides gashed with needless landslides, he felt as though a friend had been injured. This feeling he has

4

never been able to relinquish, despite the buffets of a practical world and the counsels of men of affairs.

For that reason the continent of North America is the hero of this book. The continent has been set upon by thieves and footpads and most foully hurt and beaten. Now at long last its patience is exhausted and it turns on its tormentors. The boy and the mountainside got on well together. Perhaps, when enough people understand what has been done, Americans and the broad land which so graciously offered them a home may learn to get on together too.

The Feel of America

A generation ago, only the rich and the indigent could afford to see their country, the one in a Pullman, the other in a boxcar. Today, in twenty-five million automobiles, half the population has the opportunity to look beyond the horizons of its native place. True, the view is restricted by billboards outside and by a curious apathy to any sensation save speed inside, but the chance is there, and more of us are taking it. Someday we may become a land-conscious rather than a land-blind people.

Many travelers set out to report "conditions" in the nation. By conditions they mean the temper of the citizens, their political and economic health, the strength of various movements, the outlook for presidential candidates. I propose to set out and report the temper of the land and the outlook for its perpetuation. People come and go, migrate, change their courses, disappear. The continent goes on. How is North America feeling?

5

Technically, North America includes the United States, Canada, Alaska and Mexico, as well as the adjacent islands. We shall concern ourselves primarily with the United States. Canada shares the same culture, and much that we shall say about the United States is equally applicable to the north. Mexico follows a different pattern altogether, as I have indicated at some length in another place. Alaska is too rigorous for white men, save in a few favored valleys, and is little changed from the time when brown men from Asia first landed there in their canoes.

Continental America extends for 3,000 miles from Pacific to Atlantic and 1,200 miles from the Gulf to Canada, and it covers three million square miles. Its highest point is Mt. Whitney, 14,500 feet above the level of the sea, and its lowest point Death Valley, 276 feet below—both in California. Suppose we run our hands, as it were, over a considerably magnified relief map of our country. It may give us the feel of where we live.

The left hand rests on the Pacific, the right on the Atlantic. Moving inward, the right hand encounters a coastal shelf, broken by the valleys of many rivers—the Connecticut, Hudson, Susquehanna, James, Roanoke, Savannah. Then it comes to the "fall line," where navigation on these rivers ceases, and begins to climb the Appalachian Mountains. These are ancient mountains as geology counts time, much worn with natural erosion and past ice ages. The range runs from Maine to Georgia. Along its skyline, Benton Mackaye has surveyed his famous Appalachian Trail, a thousand miles in length. This is a real trail for human feet, not a spurious "trail" for rubber tires. Chocorua belongs in the

6

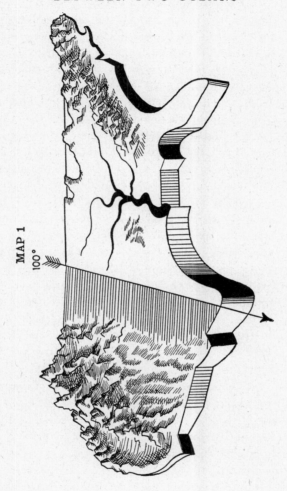

MAP 1

100°

range. The highest points are Mt. Mitchell in North Carolina, which rises to 6,700 feet, and Mt. Washington in the
north, 6,300 feet. Thumb and middle finger mark these two
nubs. The ranges we note are not solid, but pierced with
fine highland valleys, like the Shenandoah in Virginia.

The right hand then slides down to a mid-continent
plateau which dips to the five Great Lakes on the north and
to the lower Mississippi region on the south. The coastal
shelf meanwhile takes in all of Florida—which has been
described as an area 400 miles long, 100 miles wide, and four
feet high—and swings around the Gulf of Mexico over
southern Georgia and Alabama, up the Mississippi for 500
miles, and so down along the coast of Texas into Mexico—
all flat or rolling land, below 500 feet in altitude.

Let your hand explore the grooves which lead from the
Atlantic into the Mississippi Valley. By land there are only
three low paths not blocked by the Appalachian Moun-
tains: around the coastal plain in southern Georgia, down the
St. Lawrence Valley and so into the Great Lakes, up the
Hudson River Valley and west through the Mohawk
Valley to Lake Ontario. Everywhere else the hand must
climb. Everywhere else a covered wagon once had to climb.

The right hand moves across the vast flat valley of the
Mississippi, dipping into its eastern tributaries, the Ohio,
the Wabash, the Cumberland and the Tennessee, fed by the
ranges just traversed. We cross the deep groove of the
Mississippi itself, falling south in a waved line from a point
near the western tip of Lake Superior to the delta below
New Orleans. Once over the river, the flat basin begins to
tip slowly upward toward the west. The land is rising. Half-

way between the moving thumb and forefinger, a low line of mountains is felt. These are the Ozarks of Missouri, famous for hillbillies and rough-hewn poetry, the only considerable eminence in all the great valley. Except for it the plain rises smoothly, 500 feet, 1,000 feet, 2,000 feet. Rivers now flow from the west toward the central trough—the Missouri, the Platte, the Arkansas, the Red River of the south. Somewhere on the line of western Kansas, close to the Dust Bowl, right hand will meet left.

Now the left hand on the Pacific. Here the coastal shelf is a mere window ledge, notched at the mouth of the Columbia River in Oregon and at San Francisco Bay. Up the hand goes, 5,000, 10,000 feet, almost straight from the sea. Then an abrupt descent into deep valleys behind the coastal range. One of them, the Central Valley of California, is 400 miles long, and among the most productive spots on earth. Then up again to the high Sierras, to Mt. Whitney, Mt. Shasta and other giants, two and a half times as high as Mt. Mitchell. The hand is scratched with jagged peaks. It dips to the Great Basin—Salt Lake and the irrigation ditches about it lie here—a semiarid region, mostly above 5,000 feet. Across rugged Idaho, Nevada, Arizona, then up to the most massive, if not the highest, range of all: the Continental Divide, the Rockies themselves, with the loftiest peaks congregating in Colorado. As we move up these great slopes, the ball of the hand feels the sharp cleft of the Grand Canyon of the Colorado. Down into Mexico the Rockies run, and up into Canada and Alaska. They are the backbone of the continent, altogether dwarfing the Appalachian range on the east.

9

From its 10,000 foot level, with forefinger in the Yellow-stone, our left hand begins to slide downward across Montana, Wyoming, eastern Colorado, New Mexico— 8,000, 5,000, 4,000, 3,000 feet. Somewhere on the western Kansas line it meets the right hand.

If this movement could be done without words, if one could just feel the country's shape with one's hands, one might come to know the continent. The grand outline, the essence, would penetrate one's consciousness. Such inner knowledge does not come by noting on the map that it is 186 miles from Squashville to Bopptown by Route 17, and that, if one hustles, one can make it by six o'clock. As the hands move, one feels the indentations of the rivers and begins to appreciate the cardinal importance of great water-sheds in the life of the continent. State lines are only in men's heads, marks on a drawing board; watersheds are the sculpture of geological ages.

A land may be classified in many ways: By elevations— which we have just attempted; by underlying rock forma-tion—the limestones, which give good soils, shales, which give fair, sandstones, which give poor; by cover—forest, grass or desert; by rainfall, which more or less determines cover; by watershed, which provides the theater for the hydrologic cycle; by temperature and climate; by natural economic regions. Let us look more closely at natural regions, rainfall and watershed.

A *region* may be defined as an area where nature acts in a roughly uniform manner, a *section* as an area where men think in a uniform manner. The Old South is a section, but the land is cut into several natural regions whose patterns are far from uniform. A region provides a major basis for economic planning, a section a basis for political uproar.

Van Hise has outlined eight regions in America. They are not conclusive, but to list them will perhaps contribute to an understanding of our continent:

1. *The Atlantic and Gulf Plains*

An area running from Cape Cod in Massachusetts to Brownsville, Texas, on the Mexican border. It is marked generally by plentiful rainfall, good soils, heavy forests in the natural state and great swamps, such as the Everglades in Florida, the Dismal Swamp of North Carolina, the bayous of Louisiana and the coastal swamps of Texas. It extends inland to the fall line, where ships must halt and men and goods take to land transport, an important boundary before the coming of the railroads. The cotton belt is largely in this area.

2. *The Eastern Plateau*

The area above the fall line, running from Maine to Georgia. A pine country with indifferent soils and much boulder farming.

3. *The Appalachian Mountain Country and the Ozarks*

Heavy forests originally. Steep slopes. An area particularly subject to man-made erosion.

4. *The Great Lakes Plains*

An area extending around the lakes and down the east side of the Mississippi Valley. Good soils, natural forest. Corn-belt country. Heavy rainfall.

5. *The Prairie Plains*

West of the Mississippi running from eastern Dakota to eastern Texas. The breadbasket of America. Wheat and corn and hogs and beef. Tall grass was the natural cover. Twenty to forty inches of rainfall, a bit less than in regions to the east. Soils sometimes twenty feet deep. "Probably the most fertile region on earth," followed by the black lands of Russia.

6. *The Great Plains*

A continental slab tilted from the Prairie Plains up to the Rockies. Here rainfall drops below twenty inches and tall grass gives way to short. Deep, fertile soil. Grazing, dry farming, irrigation. The home of the cowboy.

7. *The Rocky Mountains and the Western Plateau*

The area includes the Great Basin. Forests and heavy rainfall on the mountains, arid valleys between. Bunch grass, sage brush, cactus. Some grazing and some irrigation. Large mineral deposits. Incomparable scenery.

8. *The Pacific*

A vertical country. Forested mountains, grass-covered valleys, rich soils. Heavy rainfall in coastal Oregon and Washington; deficient rainfall in California. Irrigation. Fruit and truck crops. Magnificent scenery. The tallest, grandest trees on the planet.

Next, let us look at rainfall. The right hand, the low-moving hand, groped its way over an area where rainfall

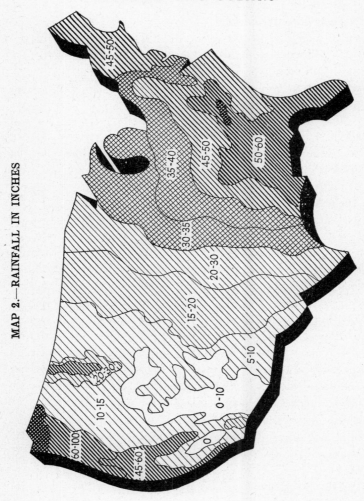

MAP 2.—RAINFALL IN INCHES

exceeded twenty inches per year. The left hand, the high hand, moved over an area where rainfall averaged under twenty inches. The dividing line runs approximately at the 100th meridian, where the two hands met, and cuts the continent in two. This is a most important line; we shall come back to it repeatedly.

The water problems of the eastern half revolve around floods, navigation, erosion, water excess. The problems of the western half—save in coastal Oregon, which has the highest rainfall on record—revolve around the questions of drought, dust storms, water deficit and shortage. Irrigation projects in the east are few, in the west many. The east was once a land primarily of forest, the west one of grass.

The annual rain and snow fall in America amounts to 1,500 cubic miles of water, five billion acre feet, the equivalent of ten Mississippi Rivers in their courses. Two-thirds of it falls on the right-hand half; only one-third on the left half. As rainfall begins to decline, moving west from the Mississippi, forest gives way to tall prairie grass, which in turn gives way to the short hardy grass of the Great Plains, which gives way to sagebrush, greasewood and cactus of the Great Basin. In Nebraska it takes fifteen acres to raise one beef "critter," in the sagebrush country 50 to 200 acres. The average man drinks a little over a ton of water in a year; a bushel of corn drinks ten to twenty tons; a pound of beef requires fifteen to thirty tons, directly and indirectly. Water is the life blood of the continent, especially of the west.

The Appalachians, being low old mountains, do not impede the moisture-bearing winds from the Atlantic and

14

the Gulf of Mexico. Rain falls heavily on the eastern part of the Mississippi Valley. Winds from the Pacific, however, lose their moisture on the high coastal ranges and the Rockies; rainfall on the Great Basin and the Great Plains is restricted. It is most fortunate for the United States that North America has no transverse mountain range comparable to the Himalayas. Such a range would divorce the middle west from the mild, damp Gulf winds and cause arid or semiarid conditions in all our north central states. Other continents— Asia, Africa, Australia—have dry centers and fabulous deserts. Not so North America—yet. But a few more generations of the course we have pursued will produce man-made deserts which will have few rivals in other continents.

Europe is a good continent but its natural regions and boundaries have been seriously disrupted by rival political states. Europe was settled with broadaxe and sweat at a snail's pace over centuries; America, west of the Appalachians, was settled with railroads and steam, at a gallop, over decades. This difference in the tempo of settlement, according to Zimmerman, accounts for the profound differences between European and American institutions. Europeans are a "time people" rooted to the past; Americans and Canadians are a "space people" with no strong local roots. But Mexicans, like Europeans, are a time people with ancient civilizations behind them. The American culture is an experiment in transportation. Extreme distances weaken its resource pattern. This is why we whoop it up for railroads, motorcars and speed. "In many cases, the automobile is not a sign of excessive prosperity, but a means of overcoming America's greatest handicap, the excess of space."*

Finally, let us look at the continental watersheds. The Mississippi basin drains more than half the area of the nation. Its eastern arms take the runoff from the Appalachians, its western arms that from the Rockies. Each main stream constitutes a mighty basin in itself, but all are linked together in one colossal drainage system; all contribute to the acute problem of floods in the lower Mississippi. The Tennessee Valley Authority is now seeking to tame one stream. The resulting techniques, if happy, may be applied to other tributaries, and even to Old Man River himself.

From the eastern slopes of the Appalachians flow a series of short, rapid rivers which, while presenting interesting problems, are less important for the welfare of the continent and of man. (That these rivers need taming, however, a wild Merrimac and Connecticut recently showed.) North of them the St. Lawrence, draining the Great Lakes, constitutes another strategic basin. It lays its problems of navigation, power, drainage and lake levels jointly on the doorsteps of the United States and Canada. Another joint charge is the Red River of the North, linking Minnesota with Manitoba and Lake Winnipeg. The Rio Grande is the twin concern of the United States and Mexico. It has been viciously mishandled as we shall see. In the far west, two rivers are outstanding: the Columbia in the north, and the Colorado in the south. Boulder Dam on the Colorado is the concern of seven states, as well as of the whole nation, while for the last seventy-five miles of its course to the Gulf of California,

* E. W. Zimmerman: *World Resources and Industries.* Harper & Brothers, 1933.

16

the river runs through Mexico. Another basin of great importance is the Central Valley of California, with its two rivers, the Sacramento on the north, the San Joaquin on the south, joining in the center of the valley to meet the Pacific at San Francisco Bay.

Man has long addressed his survival to great rivers—the Nile, the Tigris and Euphrates, the Hwang Ho, the Ganges, the Danube and the Volga. With their cooperation civilizations rise, the wheat springs, trade flows, great cities grow. If their laws are forgotten or neglected, civilizations fall, floods roar, silt chokes the channels, bread fails, drought spreads. North America is no exception to this ancient rule. The continent has given us much and will give us more, if we work with her. But if we continue our neglect and contempt for her land and waters, she will exact a calamitous penalty, and all the laboratories, all the machines, all the banks, will not offset it.

Chapter II

THE PRIMEVAL CONTINENT

WHEN the continent of North America rose dripping from the sea, the sun looked down on a vast expanse of naked rock. As millenniums passed, according to geologists, wind, water, temperature and all the forces of natural erosion cracked the rock and laid down the beginnings of the soil. Plants, originating we know not where, crept into the crevices and added their vegetable decay. Animal life appeared, again from the unknown, fed on the plants, and left its flesh and bones to the soil.

Soil

Heat, light and gravity were the fundamental forces; air, water, ice and plant and animal organisms were the agents. Air oxidized the mineral particles; water hydrated them; bacteria, worms, plants, all assisted in the disintegration and decomposition of the rocks. Thus by a complex and age-long process, the soil was made. The surface layer with its humus, manufactured by thousands of generations of plants as they died and decayed, is the most precious of all the continent's resources. Here nature has prepared for active growth. Here we find six per cent organic matter. Twelve inches down, organic matter drops to three per cent; three feet down, it falls to one per cent.

Loam soil is one-quarter water, one-quarter air, one-tenth organic matter. "It thus swims, breathes, and is alive." Nitrogen, phosphorus and potassium are the three great plant foods—you buy your fertilizer by formula, 4-8-8 or 8-3-5, with the numbers representing the minerals in that order—but soil also contains magnesium, sulphur, iron, carbon and other minerals. Roots of plants select what they need and drink it up, dissolved in water. Above the ground, the action of light and heat enables the plant leaves, through an extraordinary process called *photosynthesis*, to take in oxygen and carbon from the air and manufacture starches and sugars for cellulose, the backbone of growing things.

At least three ice ages have been traced in North America. At the time they blighted life and seemed only agents of destruction. But nature's processes are long. As the ice cap ground down from the Arctic, it pulverized the surface rocks. In the last advance the frozen barrier ran from Long Island to St. Louis, and then in a great arc up to Montana. Trees and plants were driven to mountain tops. As the barrier retreated, the trees spread slowly down the slopes to find deposits of new potential soil in the valleys and plains where the glaciers had lain. The exchange between mineral and vegetable began again at an accelerated pace. But as men count time, the pace was slow. It has been estimated that one inch of top soil was laid down every 500 years. In some places it took 1,000 years.

When the dark humus is formed under a cover of forest,

19

rain ferments it, and the minerals tend to be carried down into the earth, leaving the top soil acid. On arid plains fermentation is less, minerals stay near the surface and soils tend to be alkaline. The high mineral content is the reason why irrigation often produces bumper crops from apparent deserts. The soils of the natural grasslands are neutral and best of all for farming. Grass roots go deep and rot where they die, forming a mulch which absorbs and holds water. Runoff and scouring are reduced to a minimum. The result is a layer of deep soil of great fertility. The tall grass prairies of Iowa and Nebraska, the breadbasket of America, attest it.

Soil is like a bank account—in a happy land where bank failures are unknown. Under natural conditions plants and animals die and return to the earth what they have taken, plus a margin to spare. Deposits exceed withdrawals, as we have seen, at the rate of about one inch of soil for every 500 years of time.

Under handicraft conditions, before the coming of the machine, farm wastes and manures returned minerals to the soil at about the same rate as they were taken out. In the case of phosphorus the supply is so limited that if it should not be constantly returned "a single century would be sufficient to produce a disastrous reduction in the amount of life." A balance is struck, but the soil seldom receives an increment under primitive agricultural conditions. A possible exception is the soil of England, which some students believe to be better now than in Roman days, owing chiefly to the use of cover crops of grass and pasture. The pastures have been grazed for centuries but not overgrazed.

So we have a slowly growing bank account under primeval conditions, a balanced account under handicraft conditions. But when commercial agriculture comes into the picture, with its one-crop farming and maximum exploitation of the land, the formula changes suddenly. Minerals go out of the soil, out over the railroads and highways in boxcars and crated foodstuffs to the cities, and they never come back. The bank balance steadily shrinks. Bare ground left by the plow will lose as much soil in ten years as unbroken prairie in 4,000 years. Artificial fertilizer helps, but, as we shall see, the return from this source is pitifully inadequate.

Waters

In 1630 the American soil was building, the bank account growing. Rivers, except the Mississippi and the Colorado in spring freshet, ran clear and sparkling to the oceans. Side banks were carved, new channels opened from time to time, but the tangle of forest roots and the thick matted grasses held the soil of the hillsides firmly in place. Average rainfall was probably not different from what we know today, but nature by every possible device kept the water on or in the land. The litter on the forest floor, grasses, herbs, shrubs, rotting logs, twigs, leaves, flowers, even rocks and pebbles, all retarded the runoff of the rains and snows. One hundred pounds of sand will absorb twenty-five pounds of water; one hundred pounds of clay, fifty pounds of water; but one hundred pounds of humus will absorb two hundred pounds of water, twice its own weight. The slowly building humus lay deep over the continent.

Low-lying flat lands had become swamps and marshes.

21

The industrious beaver, first of conservation planners, was patiently making more swamps. Pockets and depressions, many of them scooped out by the glaciers of the ice ages, became ponds and lakes. The rain which soaked into the humus filtered in due course to vast underground artesian basins, of which eight have been especially marked by scientists:

1. The St. Peter Sandstone Basin, underlying Minnesota, Iowa, Illinois and Missouri.
2. The Dakota Sandstone Basin, under the Dakotas and Nebraska.
3. The Marshall Sandstone Basin, under southern Michigan.
4. The Atlantic Coastal Basin, running from New Jersey to Florida.
5. The Gulf of Mexico Coastal Basin.
6. The Southern California Basin.
7. The San Joaquin Basin, underlying central California.
8. The Roswell Basin, under New Mexico, the most productive single basin known.

In addition there were many smaller catch pools. Perhaps your artesian well taps one of them. These underground waters, together with the surface lakes, ponds and marshes and the spongy, absorptive humified soil, formed great natural reservoirs which held the cloudbursts, the freshets and the melting snows of spring, stored the surplus waters snugly underground or on the surface, reduced the flood crests and released the surplus slowly over the dry seasons. The artesian basins alone held many years' supply. Without them, nearly all rivers and streams would go dry at times.

22

Here we have a great balanced device for keeping the inflow and outflow of water in equilibrium. It operated in all the chief watersheds. Although floods were known before the white man, not only was their violence restrained in the headwaters by natural reservoirs but in their lower courses they normally overflowed into wide plains which again broke their destructive force. Nothing speeds a flood like walling it in levees. River channels meanwhile were curved and meandering, which further checked the rush of waters to the sea.

The ways of water underground are mysterious, as miners and visitors to limestone caverns know. We shall have a good deal to say about water, both above ground and below, in the chapters to come, and it will be well to give the scientific classification at this point.

Surface waters include wet lands, swamps, marshes, ponds, lakes, creeks, rivers and the ocean.

Superficial ground water is that held and absorbed by the humified soil. When its "field moisture capacity" is reached, the surplus infiltrates deeper. The roots of plants tap this superficial layer.

Ordinary ground water is the next zone below, usually in loose material resting on rock. Sometimes there are a number of zones, one under the other. Dug wells tap this area.

Artesian water lies still deeper, although the demarcation from ground water is not always exact. Generally it occurs in a definite and extensive geological structure, as in the eight basins named above. Sometimes the basin is under pressure like a petroleum pool. Driven wells tap these waters. The infiltration may be at a point far distant from the

23

point where they are tapped. Artesian waters are great wanderers, and are not attentive to nice legal distinctions between state and federal authority. They obey the laws of nature, not of man.

Forest

Of the two billion acres of America in 1630, it is estimated that almost half, or just short of a billion acres, was in forest, thirty-eight per cent in strong grasses, eleven per cent in the shrubs and vegetation of arid plains, and only two and a half per cent in outright desert.

From the Atlantic to well beyond the Mississippi, and covering all the south, stretched an almost unbroken primeval forest. A squirrel might leap from bough to bough for a distance of a thousand miles and see scarcely a flicker of sunlight on the ground, so contiguous were the tree crowns and so dense the foliage. The three great western mountain ranges were covered with forests to the timber line, and both California and the Pacific northwest had their stands of lordly conifers. The giant sequoia trees of California, some measuring thirty feet in diameter, with 4,000 annual growth rings, were among the oldest living things in the world, and perhaps the most majestic. The Douglas fir of Oregon grew to eight feet in diameter and towered 300 feet above the ground; Sitka spruces measured up to twelve feet in diameter; redwoods reached seventeen feet in diameter. In the eastern forests, white pines were found nine feet in diameter, rising straight and true for 200 feet. On some of them was later to be hewn the "broad arrow of the king," which marked them for the British navy.

24

MAP 3.—NATIVE VEGETATION, 1630

Oaks grew up to nine feet in diameter; tulip poplars, ten feet; bald cypresses, twelve feet.

The original forests included a variety of useful timber unequalled anywhere on earth. More varieties were to be found in the tropics and larger contiguous areas of woodland existed in Russia, but nowhere could be found so vast an area covered with such variety of species. More than half of the stand was in soft woods—pine, fir, spruce, hemlock. There were more than 500 native species, excluding the subtropical trees of Florida, 100 of which had important lumber uses.

It is reported that Lief Ericsson, sailing down the New England coast, was much impressed with the timber of Vineland. Thorwald, in 1005, brought back a shipload to Norway. De Soto marveled at the trees of Florida. Jaques Cartier, coasting up the St. Lawrence, observed that the land was "full of all sorts of goodly trees, Cedars, Firres, Ashes, Boxe, and Willows." But Captain John Smith in Virginia struck the practical note. The country, he said, was "overgrown with all sorts of excellent good woodes for building houses, boats, barks and shippes." On the other hand, we must never forget that the forest had an even more important function: to hold the waters back in their run to the oceans.

Grass

Beyond the Mississippi, forest cover gave way to grass cover, with less rainfall but perhaps even richer soil. Many hymns have been sung to trees, but grass, which meant so much to the vitality and beauty of the continent, has been neglected. The waving grasses of the prairie covered one-sixth of all America, tall, luxuriant and deep rooted. In the spring the whole area was a sea of flowers—phlox, shooting stars and violets among the sturdier and slower growing species. Across these meadows, which stretched to the horizon, the buffalo moved in herds ten thousand strong.

Farther west we reach mid-continent, the twenty-inch rainfall line, where the grasses begin to shorten—waist high, knee high, ankle high. The short grass of the Great Plains covered an empire almost as broad as that of the tall grass of the prairies. Here grew grama, galleta, buffalo, wire, and other native grasses, sturdily holding the soil against wind and water. Scientists now search the region for surviving bunches of species which once covered hundreds of square miles. In dry years the plains looked like an endless smooth carpet; in wet years taller plants mixed with the shorter and gave the pattern more variety.

Still farther west, in the arid regions of the Great Basin, as well as to the south, where the mountains blocked off moisture, other types were found, adapted through the centuries to live with a minimum of water. Here were the bunch grass, sagebrush, mesquite, creosote bush, greasewood and many others. They spread a mat over the dry plateaus, held the sands in place, and at certain seasons were radiant with flowers.

Creatures

There were few men on the primeval continent, but the land was covered with trails. In Kentucky, where the buffalo came over the mountains to the salt licks and meadows, their paths were broad enough to drive three wagons abreast, as settlers later found. From the Blue Ridge to the Rockies

27

spread a network of thoroughfares laid out with a canniness which a builder of railroads might envy—following well-watered glades, natural meadows, beaver meadows, intervales; crossing the mountains along the heights of land where trees were thinnest. These were the roads of America's inhabitants before the white men.

In the forest from coast to coast lived deer, elk, moose and bear. Elk had their highways from the Allegheny Mountains, through the Adirondacks, north into Quebec. Another great road system ran from the Great Lakes to Vancouver; another north and south along the Rocky Mountains from Canada to Mexico. Antelope grazed the plains along with the buffalo, whose range was wider. Buffalo ran from the Great Smokies to the Rockies, north to Great Slave Lake and down to Central Mexico. The beaver built his dams from Atlantic to Pacific, an engineer of little waters. It was sad that one so industrious and useful should have been the first to go, to make stiff, ugly stovepipe hats.

On the high peaks were mountain goat and mountain sheep, clinging with airy grace to the edges of eternity. In the marshes, wild turkey, grouse, wild swan, duck, shorebill, rail and crane. Wild geese drove their wedges from north to south over the ancient well-marked flyways. Flights of passenger pigeons obliterated the sun. No fewer than 170 species of game birds were found in the primeval environment, and the wet lowlands which nourished the balance of the waters nourished them. Salmon leaped by the million up the Columbia; shad up the Penobscot, the Connecticut and the Delaware. Trout lay in every mountain pool. Shellfish were plentiful in all the coastal waters, depending on a delicate equilibrium between the salt of the ocean and the fresh water of the emerging rivers.

Men

The Indian population north of Mexico did not much exceed a million. Some authorities believe that in 1630 it was no greater than it is today. One of the larger estimates is divided as follows:*

United States proper	849,000
British America	221,000
Alaska	73,000
Greenland	10,000
Total	1,153,000

It is probable that Mexico was settled by a people from Asia which crossed Bering Strait, filtered down through the continent and finally developed maize and maguey on the plateaus. These products gave them a storable grain and fibers for textiles, and so the basis of a real civilization. The third leg on which civilization normally stands—a beast of burden—was not developed. The Toltecs, Maya and Aztecs reached remarkable heights with only two. Their agriculture was advanced, and revolved around what anthropologists call the corn-beans-squash complex. For two thousand years and more the Mexican diet was built on this trio. It is so built today, as the traveler quickly learns. It was a good, nourishing foundation, and gradually found its way north to the peoples above the Rio Grande.

The Indian farmers of America, in addition to corn,

* James Mooney: The Aboriginal Population of America North of Mexico. *Smithsonian Miscellaneous Collections*, vol. 80, no. 7, 1928.

beans and squash, in certain areas cultivated sweet potatoes, wild rice, strawberries and Jerusalem artichokes and gathered fruits, nuts, maple syrup and berries. Their only domestic animals were the dog and the turkey, as in Mexico. Tobacco was widely grown. The original people came down from north to south and founded a genuine civilization, the arts of which then flowed back from south to north. It is significant that the most highly developed of all American Indians, the pueblo peoples of the southwest, were those nearest to Mexico. They carried on their remarkable culture, furthermore, under difficult conditions, where water was at a premium.

Indians farmed in the south and they farmed in the north, but there was more hunting in the north. Without the maize of these northern farmers, the Pilgrim fathers would have died to a man the first winter in Plymouth. Connecticut was settled by eager gentlemen with an eye to the rich corn lands along the Connecticut and Housatonic river bottoms.

It may be stated as the general conclusion of students of American ethnology that, at the time of the discovery, the Indians of North America—with the possible exception of two or three tribes on the plains that followed the buffalo—were not nomadic, but, as a rule, were occupying well-defined areas, with sparsely settled areas between the groups.*

Maize was planted in hillocks and cultivated around the stalk; beans and squashes were sowed between the hillocks. Plows were unknown. The fields were small and rough except in the natural meadow lands of river bottoms. Food was produced not for sale but for use. As a result no serious

* McGee and Thomas: *Prehistoric North America.*

30

demands were made on the soil, in the way either of erosion or of progressive loss of mineral matter.

The Indian was not a nomadic savage but a primitive agrarian, living in settled villages, tilling the soil and hunting when the hunting was good. He had a keen sense of his dependence on the natural environment and an aversion to a needless waste of resources. He had no sense of private property in land; the group and its subsistence formed his base line. "It has been well said that in the Indian land agreements, the red man sold one thing, and the white bought a different."* When the conservation program was launched by the government in 1933, the most willing hands to be found the nation over were on the Indian reservations, "simply because group work for community benefit appeals to the Indian social instinct."† The beasts and birds of North America upheld the continental equilibrium because they were an unconscious part of it. The Indian stood aside. He was a man with brain and tools, but without machines to lend him arrogance. A sure instinct told him that it was safer to work with natural forces than against them. That instinct, battered by generations of ignominy and humiliation, still survives.

Underground

Beneath the forests and the grasses, unknown and unwanted by the people of the primeval continent, lay deposits of coal, iron, petroleum, natural gas, copper, zinc, lead, gold, silver, phosphates and many other minerals. They were changing, some of them growing in volume, but the growth

* Paul B. Sears: *Deserts on the March.* University of Oklahoma Press.
† Report of the National Resources Board.

31

and change were so slow as to be immeasurable save in geologic time. Coal deposits of varying grades underlay about one-sixth of the country. Deep-lying oil sands contained twenty-nine billion barrels of petroleum. Seven billion tons of iron ore lay locked in the mountains. Under no other area of like size on the planet was stored so much potential wealth. The minerals were static, dead, but some of them were the result of life. Coal and oil were the petrified forests and sea life of the carboniferous era. Phosphate rock was compounded of the fossilized bones of ancient animals. If the time span is taken long enough, the whole resource pattern weaves together.

Climate

The United States lies almost wholly in the north temperate zone. From the point of view of human well being, this is a resource of the first importance. The history of the world is mainly the history of temperate regions lying roughly between latitudes 30° and 60°. Near the equator life is too easy and man becomes a food *gatherer*. In temperate regions he is forced to become a food *producer*. Tropic days are all alike. There is no swing of the seasons. The sun sets at almost the same hour the year around and the cycle of life is the day. In temperate latitudes the life cycle is the year, with its stimulating changes between winter, spring, summer and fall. The preparation for winter especially causes men to take thought, plan, exert their ingenuity.

North America drives a great wedge into this zone. In South America the wedge runs the other way, and only Argentina and Chile fall into the vigorous latitudes. Europe lies almost entirely in the temperate zone, thanks in part

PLATE II.—Primeval forest. (Mississippi Valley Committee.)

to the Gulf Stream, without which Scandinavia would be as desolate as Labrador. North India, South Russia, China, Japan, South Africa (in Africa, like South America, the wedge runs the other way), South Australia, New Zealand, are temperate lands. On their surfaces the history of civilization has largely been written.

Climax

The North American continent before the coming of the white man was rich with growing things, incredibly beautiful to look upon, wild and tempestuous in its storms and climatic changes and perhaps the most bountifully endowed by nature of all the world's continents. Forest, grasses and wild life were at the maximum limit of their vitality; deserts and barren places were at a minimum.

The attainment of maximum vitality is a long, slow process. Each region finds its ultimate balance, which scientists call *climax*, where soil and plant life are at their sturdiest. The forest goes to its limit, both in geographical area and in superior types of trees. It may invade the prairie in its exuberance. Grasslands go to their limit, invading the desert, developing a climax crop with long roots to tap the under-lying water table. Desert and barren areas shrink to an absolute minimum. "A continent undisturbed by man is one of the most abundant life possible."

This then is the setting, the stage upon which the drama of conquest and settlement is to be enacted over a period of three hundred years. A high-pooped ship comes winging over the Atlantic horizon. On the dunes at the tip of Cape Cod a white-tailed deer looks curiously out to sea and turns to browse again.

33

Chapter III

FROM PLYMOUTH ROCK
TO DUCKTOWN

THE primeval setting has been explored. How does the continent look today after three hundred years of occupation? Suppose we climb into a metaphorical airplane and cruise about America, first observing the whole picture, then circling to examine this area and that, finally looking into conditions underground—with the help of whatever scientific instruments may be necessary.

The basic map has changed but little: a slit across the Isthmus of Panama, a few minor shifts in the coast line, small islands thrown up here and there or washed away, some river channels recut. But coming closer we find the cover enormously changed, as well as the denizens thereof. The old forest, the old grasslands have almost completely disappeared. Desert lands have broadened. A dust desert is forming east of the Rockies where firm grass once stood. Woodlands—and a spindly lot they are by comparison—cover only half the area the primeval forest once covered. Grazing areas are still immense but the old types of native grasses have largely gone.

34

On one-quarter of continental United States are new fields, bare in the winter, green with crops in the summer. Adjacent to these tilled fields are pasture lands, unknown before, of an almost equal area. On some of the old arid grasslands irrigation ditches now run, and between them is the green of crops. This is particularly noticeable around Salt Lake in Utah, in regions of the southwest, in the Imperial and Central valleys of California. Scattered about the continent, especially along the rivers and the sea coasts, are the black clusters of cities and the smaller dots of towns and villages. Linking them run a million miles and more of highways, railroads, the tracery of power lines, and pipe lines underground. Comparing the new with the old, in round figures:

THE AMERICA OF 1630*

	Millions of Acres
Dense primeval forest	820
Native grass lands—tall and short	600
Open woodlands, arid lands, mountain tops, etc	430
Desert	50
Total	1,900

THE AMERICA OF 1930

Merchantable forest—not all virgin	150
Cut-over forest—growing	200
Cut-over forest—dying	100
Farm woodlands	150
Grazing lands—open	330
Farm crop lands (irrigated, 25 million)	400
Farm pasture lands, etc	420
Urban lands	50
Desert and waste	100
Total	1,900

* United States without Alaska.

35

Most of these figures are rough estimates, but they serve to show in a general way the changes which have taken place. Forest and native grasslands have given way to farm lands, both crop and pasture. The total farm land, including farm wood lots, approaches a billion acres, or about half the whole area. In 1630 the only parallel was the stick-furrowed fields of the Indians, which probably did not amount to a million acres all told.

Looking closer still, we see that the Indians are now clustered on a few reservations, largely in the west. On the lands over which they once hunted and grew their corn, 130 million aliens have settled, some black, some brown, but mostly white. The great herds of wild game have been replaced by domestic animals and fowl. Finally we note that in many sections the earth is pierced with holes—the shafts of mines, open-pit operations, the long drills of oil and gas and water wells.

Primeval forest, virgin soil and the waving prairie grasses have given way to open fields, harnessed rivers spanned by steel bridges, tunneled mountains, irrigated arid lands, culm banks, oil fields, canals, drained marshes and roaring, smoky cities. Beauty has been lost, we cry, but progress gained. Wild landscape has been replaced by cultured.

Soil

We drop 10,000 feet and look closer still. If this be progress, it is bitter tonic. The continental soil, the center of vitality, is visibly and rapidly declining. The forest cover has been stripped and burned and steadily shrinks. The natural grass

36

cover has been torn to ribbons by steel plows and the hooves of cattle and sheep. The skin of America has been laid open. Streams have lost their measured balance, and, heavy with silt, run wild in flood to the sea at certain seasons, to fall to miserable trickles in the drier months. This land may be bristling with tall chimneys and other evidences of progress, but it has lost its old stability.

The humus is going, and when it is gone natural life goes. Two powerful agents are destroying the soil: erosion and the loss of fertility due to mining the soil for crops. Soils which have been building steadily for 20,000 years since the last ice age now in a single century lose the benefits of several thousand years of accumulation. Corn yields in sections of Iowa have dropped from 50 to 25 bushels per acre within the lifetime of a man not yet old. This, remember, is the richest soil in America. In the northern humid states alone, scientists estimate that one-quarter of the original nitrogen, one-fifth of the phosphorus, one-tenth of the potassium and one-third of the sulphur have gone.* The carrying capacity of pasture lands declined seriously between 1919 and 1929, according to the National Resources Board.

The three billion tons of solid material washed out of the fields and pastures of America every year by water erosion contains forty million tons of phosphorus, potassium and nitrogen. This of course is in addition to losses through cropping. To load and haul away this incomprehensible bulk of rich farm soil would require a train of freight cars 475,000 miles long, enough to girdle the planet nineteen times at the equator. Approximately 400 million tons of solid earth is

* Henry A. Wallace in the *New York Times*, Mar. 29, 1936.

dumped into the Gulf of Mexico by the Mississippi alone—
the greater part of it super-soil, richer than that of the Nile.
Plant food can be restored to soil that has been worn lean
by cropping, but when water takes the soil itself—minerals,
humus, microscopic organisms, everything—only nature can
restore fertility to that land, and her rate under primeval
conditions, as we have seen, is one inch in 500 years.

One hundred million acres of formerly cultivated land has
been essentially ruined by water erosion—an area equal to
Illinois, Ohio, North Carolina and Maryland combined—
the equivalent of 1,250,000 eighty-acre farms. In addition,
this washing of sloping fields has stripped the greater part of
the productive top soil from another 125 million acres now
being cultivated. Erosion by wind and water is getting under
way on another 100 million acres. More than 300 million
acres—one-sixth of the country—is gone, going or beginning
to go. This, we note, is on land originally the most fertile.

Kansas farms are blowing through Nebraska at an accelerating rate. In the spring of 1934, the farms of the Dust
Bowl—which includes western Oklahoma, western Kansas,
eastern Colorado, the panhandle of Texas and parts of
Wyoming—blew clear out to the Atlantic Ocean, 2,000
miles away. On a single day 300 million tons of rich top
soil was lifted from the Great Plains, never to return, and
planted in places where it would spread the maximum of
damage and discomfort. Authentic desert sand dunes were
laid down. People began to die of dust pneumonia. More
than nine million acres of good land has been virtually
destroyed by wind erosion, and serious damage is reported
on nearly 80 million acres.

38

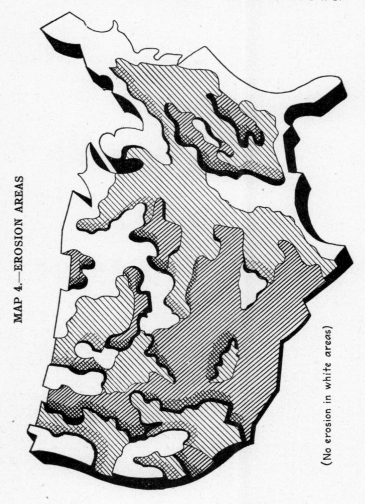

MAP 4.—EROSION AREAS

(No erosion in white areas)

Taking the continent as a whole, it is reliably estimated that half of its original fertility has been dissipated by these various agents. The rate of loss tends to follow the laws of compound interest. The stricken areas grow cumulatively larger.

Soil losses due to cropping are the result of foolish marketing procedures, revolving around the one-crop system in cotton, corn, tobacco and wheat. Losses due to erosion are the direct result of stripping the forest and grass cover from the slopes. When the tangle of roots, the sod of the native grasses, gives way to bare plowed fields with cultivated rows running up and down hill, there is nothing to hold the rain. It tears over the contours, taking the soil with it.

Forest

Not more than one-tenth of the old virgin forest remains. The Douglas firs of the Pacific northwest are the last great stand of primeval timber. We see them coming down by high-power logging machinery, and, when they have fallen, much of the area is so devastated that trees will not grow again. The soil itself is often burned in the ensuing fires. When new vegetation starts, if at all, it is a different and poorer tree crop. These cut-over, burned-over lands are still called "forest" on the maps, but we see that almost 100 million acres is really dead land—totally unknown in the old America. This is a strange and desolate phenomenon— no farms, no productive forest, no animals, no life. In 1871, 400 square miles were burnt over in Wisconsin and 1,500 people were killed. In 1927, 158,000 forest fires were reported, and they consumed nearly 40 million acres. Meanwhile we note that lumbermen are cutting trees of saw-timber size almost five times as fast as the stands are growing. In 1630 the reserves were 7,000 billion board feet; today the total has shrunk to 1,600 billion. In a generation or less, at this rate of exploitation, there will be no more reserves. Wheat crops ripen every year, sometimes oftener; lumber crops ripen every century on the average.

Grass

Some virgin timber still remains; it takes patient search to find virgin grasslands. The primeval sod has been burned, overgrazed, plowed up and destroyed. Where dry farming for wheat has been practised on the Great Plains, the Dust Bowl spreads. Where corn has been planted on the slopes in the tall grass regions, water erosion spreads. The sharp hooves of too many cattle and the close cropping of the grass by too many sheep have torn the cover from the open grazing lands, loosened the ancient sod, and started the gullies and dunes of both water and wind erosion. One hundred and sixty-five million acres of grazing lands has been seriously depleted. As in the case of forests, when new vegetation secures a foothold, the species is inferior to the old climax crop.

Waters

From the packed earth of the crop lands, the bare-burned slopes of the devastated forests, the broken sods of the grasslands, rain and melting snow rush to the rivers in a fraction of the time they used to take. In some watersheds runoff which should require three months is carried down to

41

the sea in a month. The rivers run red with mud where once they were clear. Reservoirs are filled, power dams rendered increasingly impotent. Lower a bucket into the Canadian River and allow it to settle. One-quarter of the water turns out to be rich soil which the upstream owner paid for in cash.

The baked earth of the tilled fields prevents the rain from percolating into the artesian basins as it used to percolate through the cover of forest and grass. We see the underground water table falling all over the western half of the continent. In the Dakotas and Iowa the drop is serious; in the Central Valley of California, it is still more serious. Meanwhile pumping for irrigation helps to exhaust the basins. The cool, dark reservoirs which once did so much to equalize flood and drought are sinking. The same is happening with surface reservoirs. Marshes and swamps have been drained in the hope of reclaiming good agricultural land. Sometimes the land is good and sometimes it is bad, unsuited for crops. When it is bad, fires course through the dried underbrush, as in the sterile Wisconsin and Minnesota marshes.

In the lower reaches of the rivers, the old natural side reservoirs have been blocked off by levees. Here is rich farm land, to be sure, but the rivers rise as the silt sinks, and the levees must rise higher still. In New-Orleans at flood crests, the Mississippi runs high above the streets of the town. River channels are straightened and further aid the rush to the ocean. Levees break; indeed the whole levee system nears its breaking point as a practicable engineering method for flood control.

Floods under these conditions must grow worse; droughts

42

must grow worse. The safeguards of nature have been stripped away. In times of low water, the pollution of streams becomes an ominous menace. Each community in the watershed area dumps its untreated sewage into the drinking supply of the town below. When the river is low, sewage poisons remain unoxidized.

In uncounted streams, fish lie killed by the wastes of cities and the black refuse of mine and factory. Pollution has destroyed more fish than all the fishermen, and silt has killed more than pollution. When the sun cannot get through because of the mud, the tiny water plants die and fish lose their basic food supply. Oil wastes strangle the fish fry when they come to the surface. Sewage competes with marine life for a limited oxygen supply. Waxy sludge coats the river bottoms and kills plants there. Our streams, according to Sears, have become watery deserts, inimical to life. Simpletons try to restock them. "To release millions of fingerlings into such an environment and expect them to live is like driving a flock of yearlings into Death Valley. . . . "

The catch of Pacific halibut and salmon fell steadily to 1930. Now strenuous measures of conservation are reversing the trend. The Atlantic salmon has gone, unless there be a lonely school wandering the Penobscot. The Atlantic shad is greatly reduced and fishing villages are left stranded. The shellfish catch is only a fraction of what it used to be. Oysters are splendid typhoid carriers and city sewage is rank with typhoid bacilli. The extreme low-water stages of the rivers, induced by the failure of the natural reservoirs, have caused salt water to back up into the river mouths, killing rich colonies of shellfish by encouraging enemies which thrive in greater salinity.

Creatures

The last passenger pigeon died in the Cincinnati Zoo in 1914, the sole survivor on earth of the "most abundant and the most beautiful of all American game birds." Toward the end, a single season's slaughter in Michigan accounted for five million of these creatures. The last heath hen died on Martha's Vineyard in 1932. Recently Mr. William Finley, naturalist and wild-life photographer, exhibited two films of the lower Klamath region in Oregon. The first was taken in 1915 and showed a great watershed swarming with game birds and migratory waterfowl. The second was taken twenty years later and showed the same area despoiled by promoters, a biological desert devoid of water, food or cover and forsaken by the birds which once lived and nested there. Birds, it must never be forgotten, are the chief enemies of insects. Without their protection plant life and animal life are thrown out of equilibrium, while life for man speedily becomes unendurable.

The beaver builds his dams no more, save in a few protected localities. One such may be seen as a kind of museum piece in Bear Mountain Park near New York. "First among the natural resources to fall under the American plan were the fur-bearing animals. Business enterprise has run through that range with exemplary thoroughness and expedition and has left the place of it bare. It is a neat, compact and concluded chapter."* The buffalo was not far behind. "In

* Thorstein Veblen: *Absentee Ownership and Business Enterprise in Recent Times.* Viking Press, 1923.

44

1872 the buffalo abdicated. Under the combined forces of progress as represented by the Union Pacific Railroad, the repeating rifle, and the big game hunter, those ancient Americans vanished from the earth, leaving their hides in the harness rooms of Boston, their skulls to the mercy of the sun, and their feeding grounds to cows."* I can remember as a little boy my grandfather tucking me into the open sleigh on cold winter days with a buffalo robe. One of the uses of the repeating rifle in the hands of the United States Army in the last century was to slaughter buffaloes so that the livelihood of the plains Indians would be taken from them, thus killing two birds with one bullet.

Underground

Looking below the cover of the continent we read the same story. The bowels of the earth have been cleft and robbed. Deposits painfully laid down over geological time are coming up through smoking black scars in the earth's crust to be burned, pounded, fabricated and rusted and eventually to vanish. Gold and silver mines have stripped away the accumulation of ages, and in placer mining have destroyed the surrounding soil as well. The sulphur fumes of copper refineries blast the vegetation of whole counties, as we shall presently see in detail. Phosphate mines destroy thousands of acres of surface soil. Coal pillars are pulled underground and farms fall in. Suffocating fires burn in abandoned mines for decades. In a single year enough petroleum and natural gas are exhausted to account for a million years of natural accumulation. A billion cubic feet of gas

* *Fortune Magazine.* November, 1935.

is daily blown into the air, "enough," says the National Resources Board, "to supply the United Kingdom twice over. It is forty times as much gas as all the Scandinavian countries use together. It is almost enough to supply every householder in the United States now consuming either natural or manufactured gas." Petroleum, copper, lead and zinc move toward exhaustion within a generation at the present rate of exploitation.

The following table indicates the story, using the best estimates now available. Lumber has been included with the minerals to round out the picture.

MINERAL AND TIMBER RESERVES OF THE UNITED STATES

Item	Unit	Estimated original reserve	Estimated present reserve	Taken out	Percentage exhausted
Iron	Tons	7,000,000,000	5,000,000,000	2,000,000,000	28
Copper	Tons	44,000,000	21,000,000	23,000,000	52
Lead	Tons	30,000,000	10,000,000	20,000,000	66
Zinc	Tons	26,000,000	11,000,000	15,000,000	58
Gold	Ounces	250,000,000	50,000,000	200,000,000	80
Oil	Barrels	29,000,000,000	13,000,000,000	16,000,000,000	55
Coal, anthracite	1,000 tons	22,000,000	17,000,000	5,000,000	23
Coal, bituminous	1,000 tons	2,230,000,000	2,230,000,000	20,000,000	1
Saw timber	1,000 board feet	7,000,000,000	1,700,000,000	Net loss 5,300,000,000	76

The critical mineral resources are copper, lead, zinc and petroleum. There is plenty of iron and coal still in the bins of the continent, but much of it is either of low grade or difficult to get at. The rich accessible veins have been deeply

46

mined. Gold is almost gone, but is unimportant save for decorative and magical purposes. It should be further noted that the heaviest drains have come in the last few decades. By and large, we have lost more minerals since 1900 than in all the preceding years. Only lumber was seriously reduced in the last century.

Landscape

Besides the material and financial loss here represented, an environment lovely to the eye has been sacrificed. The most hideous spots are the environs of mines and the slums and industrial areas of great cities. Gashed earth, culm banks, dead trees and streams putrid with chemicals, refuse and coal dust distinguish the mines. Cities seem to pride them-selves on turning their river banks or waterfronts into majestic privies. Here cluster smoking dumps high as Bunker Hill, gas works, sewer outlets, dilapidated coal sheds, switch yards, oil refineries, slaughterhouses, glue factories, tanneries which stun the nose and great barges laden down with garbage. Yet these waters determined the location of the city in the first place, and have often been its chief builder and nourisher. Can ingratitude go farther? European cities respect their waters and adorn their banks with parks, boulevards and public buildings. Latin-American countries do the same. Compare the waterfront of Havana with that of Brooklyn or Hoboken.

In place of green foliage and clear water, man has brought to the continent of America stinking rivers, charred forests, the incomparable filth of cities, the wretched shacks of tenant farmers along Tobacco Road. *Endothia Parasitica*,

47

the chestnut blight, killed nearly every chestnut tree from the Atlantic to the Pacific. He was an amateur, and should take lessons from the white-faced blight!

In the Year 2000

If this devastation continues at the same rate in the future as in the past, another twenty years will give us deserts, ominous and terrible. The Central Valley of California will presently become a desert if pumps continue to exhaust the falling artesian basin and if salt water continues to creep into the Delta. In fifty years the situation will be very serious indeed. Morris L. Cooke estimates that at the present rate of destruction only 150 million acres of really fertile land will then remain. This is the only acreage sufficiently level to resist erosion. And in a century?

If certain present-day trends were to be projected unaltered into the future, the map would be a sorry one. We would be compelled to show increasingly large stretches of once fertile lands stripped of their life-giving humus, rivers breaking forth in floods of increasing severity as the denuded slopes permitted an ever swifter runoff, industry and agriculture becoming ever more precarious, the life of the people on the land becoming more and more disorganized, and a steady increase of farm tenancy and economic dependency.*

Suppose present trends were to be projected unaltered into the future. I have had an opportunity to look at that future, not with a magical electric eye but with my own. In a certain area these trends have been speeded up with the

* Report of the Mississippi Valley Committee.

48

PLATE III.—Ducktown. (Photo by T.V.A. staff.)

aid of chemistry, and the future now stands stark for all to see. The normal processes of erosion are mechanical and take longer in the working out. But the end is substantially the same. The hills of the country I am about to describe are as terrible as the man-killed hills of China, but they have been blasted by the sulphuric acid fumes of a copper smelter rather than by the stripping of forest and grass.

DUCKTOWN

We left Knoxville, Tennessee, in a March snow squall and headed south along a broad concrete highway. Presently the sun came out and revealed the Great Smoky Mountains really smoking like Popocatepetl. The road passed beside a muddy river, log cabins, rail fences, steep cornfields, some of them badly gullied. At the town of Benton we turned east, steering for a 4,000-foot pass in the mountains, close to the Georgia line. The road climbed steeply up the river valley and the mountainsides drew closer. Suddenly we came upon a large concrete dam and powerhouse, beside it a steam power plant and a tourist hotel, beset with notice boards. Behind the dam in the mountain gorge was a long narrow lake called the Ocoee reservoir, in which the water was very low. This, like the hotel, the powerhouse and the road belonged to a private power company—a big, costly development.

The scenery was wild and impressive: sheer precipices, deep ravines, tumbling cascades, the gray lake. Rocks lay on the road where they had fallen from cliffs above. It must require a considerable crew to clear this road of avalanches. We turn a bend and suddenly see a thing that belongs in

49

no lake. It is a chocolate-colored tongue of shaking mud, half a mile long, and behind it are other tongues and trembling islands. These are deposits of silt, brought down by the water from the lands above. The formations are about six feet high, constantly caving in where the current strikes them. The whole upper end of the reservoir is full of them. The banks themselves have changed from good honest mud to this forbidding red-brown jelly.

We entered the narrow gorge with the river. There was hardly room for both of us. It was a river not of water but of boiling molasses. The whole stream bed, every rock, every log, every leaf of grass, was coated with silt. We passed another power plant. Across the gorge a wooden flume ran for four or five miles along the mountainside, leaping the side ravines on steel bridges. It seemed to be bearing water from some higher level. The trees about us were dead. Great charred logs thrust hideously out of the perpendicular slopes of the gorge. Mile upon mile had been blasted by fire.

Up, up, we went. Suddenly the mountain wall to the east dissolved and we looked over a broad expanse of bare rounded hills faintly green. They looked like the hills near San Francisco and seemed strangely out of place in Tennessee. Beyond the fire area were live trees again, some in their first spring raiment. Another mile and they began to die. It was not fire this time, but something still more unnatural.

We were among the rounded hills. There were bunches of withered grass on them and the occasional white skeleton of a tree. They were ribbed with cracks through which the

50

red earth appeared. In some places terracing had been attempted to hold the soil, but the terraces had long since been breached with raw open gullies. Fences fell crazily into these gulfs. The earth was opening about us; the road seemed the only firm place. Grass remained but it was functionless, its holding power gone. I cannot tell you what it means to see and feel the power of the earth cover gone. Anything might happen. Here was no place for life or for man. The gullies grew wider and deeper—twenty feet, thirty feet down, a hundred feet across. The hills burst open like a skinless dry peach. Then even the dead grass disappeared. The desolation was monstrous and complete, like mountains on the moon.

Over a crest we saw a cloud of black smoke. The road curved around the crest and Ducktown rose before us—a little village and a huge dark smelter perched on a hill. In a great circle about the smelter, measuring perhaps ten miles in diameter, every living thing had been destroyed by the sulphur fumes. These were bad lands without the balance and natural composure of a desert. Here was a wall-sided red brick schoolhouse with ten-foot gullies of livid earth leading up to it. Here a lone house with a tiny green garden, protected by heaven knows what labor and what chemistry against the sulphur. We pass a sign, WELCOME TO DUCKTOWN, and enter a huddle of wretched houses crouched under the bleak walls of the gigantic smelter, the land rushing away from every doorstep.

Inside the town, the horror is momentarily shut out. Main Street as usual—drugstore, cinema, Masonic hall, A. & P., filling station, garages, motorcars parked at proper

51

angles against the curb, people talking, shopping, smiling. COME AGAIN TO DUCKTOWN.

We halt the car at a lookout on the far side of the hill beyond the houses. Across a blasted plain on the northeast we see the far horizon with hills and trees again. Thank God for trees! We head the car for those far woodlands.

People live in Ducktown. Main Street bustles as in Middletown. Incredible. But on second thought it is the most appropriate setting for Main Street. Ugliness matches ugliness, and desolation suits desolation. A raw commercial age merits such a background, where nature throws up her hands and the good earth runs bleeding to the sea. Before it finds the ocean, it chokes the power company's reservoir. This, too, is as it should be. The true spirit of individualism. The copper company ruins the reservoir; the power company seeks whom it may devour farther down the stream.

Ducktown. The symbol of the logical end of an undirected machine age. It supports the gas stations, billboards, schoolhouses and Masonic lodges of Main Street out of the bowels of the earth with good red copper. But in the process the land has gone. Presently silt will completely fill the reservoir and no more electric power will come over the lines to Ducktown. The mine elevators will stop. Ducktown will perish. Its subterranean workers will perish. Its shacks and garages will slide into fifty-foot gullies. The belching sulphur fumes will cease. Life has gone and man must now go. The years pass. The grass begins to creep back on the edges of the desert ten miles away. After the grass come pine seedlings and oak. They come slowly, for Nature has a great wound to heal. In a thousand years, perhaps, the humus

52

will return, the streams will run clear, the great lateral cracks will be overgrown, the gullies will be filled, and earth creatures may live once more in Ducktown—where wild ducks lived before man came.

Here is the whole story of the future—"if present trends continue"—highly simplified and very clear. Metaphorically speaking, the smelter is industry, feeding on a declining resource. While that resource lasts, the people of Ducktown have jobs and automobiles. The world congratulates Ducktown on its high standard of living. Meanwhile the land crumbles away and the waters become wild and useless. This does not matter—for men without eyes—if other lands grow food and if copper keeps coming out of the mines to exchange for it. But no mine can be operated without power, and finally the outraged land and water cut off the power. What happens then? What happens when the copper runs out? What happens when other lands cease to grow crops, by virtue of Ducktowns of their own? What happens when a continent is one great Ducktown?

Chapter IV

NATURE'S BOOKKEEPING

A LOVELY vital continent has been outraged and
betrayed. But this rape of nature, while heinous, is
not a simple crime. Counsel for the defense must have his
say. To begin with, 130 million human beings could not
possibly exist in America while scrupulously respecting the
primeval equilibrium. A million Indians were about the
limit. What would men eat; how would they be clothed?
Forests had to fall, both for lumber and for tilled fields.
Wild beasts had to be decimated, their pastures given over
to domestic animals. Waters had to be put to use, irrigation
ditches dug, swamps in many areas drained. The earth had
to be laid open and minerals mined. On no other terms could
a population of this size be supported.

Whether primeval nature is a lordlier expression of life
than a restless, curious animal with a big brain and an
opposed thumb is a fair question, but irrelevant. While
I love great trees, I am more concerned with human livelihood than with the tallest tree. One is not disposed to
quarrel with the exploitation of any part of nature if it
contributes to human welfare. *But one wants to be sure that*

the exploitation throws no boomerangs. Welfare, after a fashion, has been served in the past by ravaging nature. The boomerangs are now returning thick and fast. The continent is becoming not only seriously unbalanced in natural terms but rapidly inadequate for man himself. A thousand Ducktowns may mine rich ore, but if the price is a thousand cancerous deserts it is too high.

The question before us is whether we can keep an advanced technology based on mineral exploitation and yet come to terms with nature. It is assumed that we shall continue to need 300 million acres, more or less, of good crop land, large quantities of forest products, power dams, irrigation projects, drainage, water supply, channels for navigation in inland waters, pasture lands for domestic animals, cities, highways, railroads, pipe lines—all unknown under primeval conditions. The ecology of 1630 is flatly impossible today. Can we find a new ecology which respects nature and still permits technological progress?

I believe that we can. I know that we must, or face the choice between abandoning our machines and abandoning the continent. An equilibrium must be determined and it must be planned. The first step is to understand what nature demands as a minimum; the next step is to calculate the highest possible living standards consistent therewith; the third step is to arouse the American people to bring the two together.

Henry Ford once said: "The land supports life. Industry helps man to make the land support him. When industry ceases to do that and supplants the land, and the land is forgotten and man turns to the machine for sustenance,

55

we find that we do not live off the work of our hands but off the fruits of the land." This is a wise observation which Ducktown well confirms. Broadly speaking, we have made America the most productive nation ever known by stimulating invention and consuming our resource capital. This has been the American formula. Advances in technology have kept ahead of resource decline until very recently. The depression dramatically uncovered a series of blighted areas where the resource base, considerably to our surprise, had disappeared—the cotton belt, the cut-over lands of Michigan, the Dust Bowl and many more. No mathematician would count on the two curves' offsetting one another indefinitely—a growing prosperity at the price of capital loss. Sooner or later resources were bound to decline more rapidly than random invention could close the gap.

Nature versus Science

It may be objected that invention has still a chance to win out. Why bother with soils, for instance, when Dr. W. O. Willcox announces that we could raise our present tonnage of crops on one-fifth the present acreage by an intensive use of the principles of agrobiology? Why worry about oil when motor engines can run on alcohol? Why bother about the forests when houses can be built of steel, aluminum and glass?

These again are fair questions, not to be answered by pointing tearfully to the scarred beauties of nature. If science has beaten the natural environment altogether, let us know it straight and true, weep for our trees and wild fowl if we must, but plan for a forthright scientific world.

Every such question, however, must be severely scrutinized on its merits. Let us test the three given, for they are typical.

Whether the American population could feed itself on eighty million acres of land instead of the present four hundred million is debatable in itself. Personally I tend to agree with Dr. Willcox that it is theoretically possible. Assume that it is. How does Dr. Willcox propose to operate these acres? By a tremendous program of supplementary irrigation on top of normal rainfall. Such a program calls for dependable watersheds, full artesian basins, water planning on a huge scale. Water planning calls for forest and grass cover and strict measures against erosion. Thus the instant one tries comprehensively to plan for food crops, the whole land and water complex comes in. Discount four-fifths of our crop land as ultimately needless if you will, but nature's equilibrium must still be respected to secure dependable results on the remaining fifth. There is no escape.

Geological erosion tends to be static, for soil builds as fast or a little faster than water carries it away. *Man-made erosion is dynamic and cumulative* and has no end save complete destruction. Without erosion control reservoirs will fill with silt, dams will become useless, power supplies will be shut off, floods will increase in violence, droughts and low-water periods will multiply, irrigation projects will be ruined, navigation will be disrupted, wild life will be progressively destroyed, recreation facilities will be increasingly limited. It is not a simple matter of growing food. Adequate calories might conceivably be secured by growing plants indoors in cabinets, as competent scientists have suggested.* But if we neglect the soil on the score of the food supply alone, we expose ourselves to alarming deficiencies in other economic fields, to say nothing of destroying the surface on which, after all, we must build our houses, carry on our work and contrive to live.

There is a further consideration, raised by Dr. Alexis Carrel in *Man the Unknown:*†

The staple foods may not contain the same nutritive substances as in former times. Mass production has modified the composition of wheat, eggs, milk, fruit and butter, although these articles have retained their familiar appearance. Chemical fertilizers, by increasing the abundance of crops without replacing all the exhausted elements of the soil, have indirectly contributed to change the nutritive value of cereal grains and of vegetables.

Intensive agriculture may grow a bean which satisfies the eye, but does it satisfy the stomach?

Now for question two, the substitution of alcohol for oil. Let us assume that petroleum does run low, as seems likely within a decade or two, but that engineers produce a motor which operates with reasonable efficiency on alcohol. We can still get from New York to Boston in five hours if we step on it. What does alcohol come from? From grain, potatoes or other plants. What nourishes plants? Soil and water. Furthermore, if all our present corn crop

* Dr. W. F. Gericke, plant physiologist in the University of California, is growing tomato plants fifteen feet high in shallow tanks, fed by ten chemicals in water. A wire screen holds the plant erect, its roots in the liquid. He gets 217 tons of tomatoes to the acre. He obtains 2465 bushels of potatoes to the acre by a similar method. The United States average is 116 bushels of potatoes per acre.

† Harper & Brothers, 1935.

were converted into motor fuel—to quote C. C. Furnas—. it would supply only half our present needs for motor fuel. If we are to employ alcohol as a substitute for petroleum, we shall certainly need more agricultural land rather than less.

Question three. It is true that houses can be built of steel, aluminum or glass, all common in the earth's crust. But the most important function of the forest is not to supply lumber but to protect soil, guard against floods, promote hydro-electric power, or help furnish supplementary irrigation for Dr. Willcox's intensive agricultural operations. Trees are even more useful alive than dead.

Someone raises a fourth question: the need for power dams for electricity since we have plenty of coal. This is true for the present at least. Here we enter a problem of comparative cost. If dams are needed for irrigation, navigation and flood control, the power that flows over them is substantially free. It is a pity to waste it, especially as uses for power are extremely elastic.

A fifth skeptic observes that there is no sense in worry-ing about copper because aluminum is an element so abun-dant that it will last indefinitely and can replace copper for most uses. True again, but to transform clay into aluminum requires tremendous blocks of electric power.

This all puts one in mind of a fable in Ilin's *Men and Mountains*.* Here it is, somewhat abbreviated:

THE STORY OF THE DAM BUILDERS

Suppose a power engineer began to build a dam without consulting anyone. He has found a suitable river and chosen

* Copyright, 1935, by J. B. Lippincott Company.

a suitable place and begun to work. Suddenly up comes an automobile and out jumps a man with a briefcase under his arm and says:

"I am a geologist. Stop your work at once. There is soft rock under the ground here."

There is nothing to do but to stop. The engineer orders the work stopped and the dam torn down, and sets off with the geologist to find a new place. They find a good site. The geologist is satisfied. But the first pile is scarcely driven when up comes another automobile. In it is another man with a briefcase. He jumps out and says:

"Did you think about the sturgeon and the salmon? If you build a dam here you will block their route to their spawning grounds. I am a biologist."

There's no disputing his word. This is a serious consideration. So they pull out the pile and the three of them set out to look for another site.

They find a better place. There is more power, the river bottom is solid, and the sturgeon and salmon will have no complaint to make. The work begins. But suddenly there is a cloud of dust down the road and an automobile comes into sight. In it is a man with a briefcase. Out he jumps and says:

"But how about the wheat and oats? If you build a dam here you will make the river overflow and flood hundreds of thousands of acres of valuable crops. I am an agronomist."

The engineer, geologist and biologist begin to argue with the agronomist. They argue and argue. But in the end there is nothing to do but give up and go to look for a new site.

So the four of them set out together. This time it is harder than ever to find a suitable place. Now one of them objects, now another. They hunt and hunt, but at last find a place on which all can agree.

They begin to build. They build for a month. They build for two months. Then one day there is dust down the road. Someone rolls up in an automobile. He jumps out and says:

"But how about navigation? You're going to dam up the river and make a big lake here. We shall have to have different kinds of steamers for lake traffic; river steamers won't do. We shall have to reconstruct the whole fleet. I am a director of steamship traffic."

They begin to argue again. For three whole days the engineer, the geologist, the biologist and the agronomist argue with the transport worker. They talk to him about irrigation. He parries with navigation. They talk about drainage. He answers with tonnage. They talk about excavators, he about waterways. They argue and argue, but finally set out to find a new place for the dam.

This time they hunt for a whole month before they finally find a site. Again they set to work. But another automobile comes tearing up the road. That means they will have to stop work again. This time the engineer does not wait for the newcomer to get out of the car. He takes his fountain pen and writes a telegram to the head of his department: "Must call conference of all specialists at once."

So the Great Wheel turns. No major resource question can be answered by itself, but only in relation to the galaxy, and nine times out of ten land and water appear somewhere in the cycle. That there is a tenth time, I do not deny. Some goods we can have without consulting the balance or nature. I almost cited nitrogen from the air, which can upset no conceivable equilibrium, but electric power enters here again as in the case of aluminum. The Wilson Dam at Muscle Shoals was built primarily to generate power to produce nitrates. Mr. Ford was right. However clever industry may be, the land, in its broadest sense, is the determining factor in the end. When new laboratories stand on every block and have solved every problem put to them, man will still be a creature of earth, living by sufferance of forces which he can adjust to a degree, but which he cannot ignore. Not even if he sends his rocket ships to some other world, can the ultimate control which nature imposes be thrust aside.

A Note on Ecology

Ecology may be defined as the relation of living things to their environment, or in simpler terms: Who eats what? If you put a live fish, a snail and a water plant in a globe of water, and place the bowl where the sun can strike it every day, you have what the ecologist calls a *balanced environment*.* This little world can flourish for months. Each inhabitant does his part to maintain a proper physical and chemical equilibrium. The fish lives on the plant. The plant manufactures food from the waste of the snail and the fish, and in doing so releases oxygen which purifies the water, keeping the animals from suffocating. Some of the waste from the fish is not in proper form for the plant, so the snail must prepare it. If the snail is left out, the little cosmos will soon go bankrupt.

* Following Paul Sears.

In pools and streams the same laws hold, but are more complicated to follow. Big fish feed on smaller fish and so on down the line. The smallest fish feed on insect larvae, tiny crustaceans, worms and other minute creatures, who in turn feed on microscopic water plants. It is absolutely essential that the sun come through the water, for without its energy plants can neither manufacture food nor release oxygen. The clearer the water, the better the plant factory. If the water runs heavy with silt or if it contains metallic poisons or if sewage steals oxygen from the plants for fermentation, the stream world goes bankrupt.

Similar rules obtain for the land world and for the relations between the land and water worlds; they hold for birds and beasts as well as for fishes. They hold for man—however much he may be given to declaiming in editorials and Sunday supplements about the Conquest of Nature by Humankind.

A harmonious relation to the land is more intricate and of more consequence to civilization than the historians seem to realize. Civilization is not, as they often assume, the enslavement of a stable and constant earth. It is a state of *mutual and interdependent cooperation* between human animals, other animals, plants and soils, which may be disrupted at any moment by the failure of any of them. Land spoliation has evicted nations and can do it again. As long as six virgin continents awaited the plow, this was perhaps no tragic matter. . . .*

Wherever an ecologist may wander on the planet, he can find evidences of this interrelationship. Here are a few picked at random:

* A. Leopold, in *Journal of Forestry*, October, 1933.

Saxaul trees grow in deserts. They have no leaves but their boughs are green. They have become so acclimated to lack of rainfall that if you water one of them it will die.

In East Africa overgrazing has led to serious erosion and desert conditions except where the tsetse fly has kept the cattle population down. Thus a curse to the cattle industry has preserved the long-term welfare of the land.

A potato blight on the upper Yangtze River in China saved grass and forest from being turned into plowed fields, and so protected the people farther down the valley from additional floods.

The boll weevil by ruining cotton has forced many farmers in the south to diversify their crops, to their lasting benefit.

Plants and insects get along fairly well together under primeval conditions. Cultivated fields upset the harmony and insects multiply rapidly. They become crop specialists: corn borers, boll weevils, potato beetles, sugar-beet leaf hoppers, citrophilus mealy bugs, fruit flies. "The greatest ecologic problem confronting mankind today," says Bernard Jaffe, "is to learn enough about insects so that we will have control over them."

When the bumblebee started on the road to extinction in the United States, queen bees had to be imported from Russia. They saved the 1934 clover crop. Insects are not all harmful. Observe the silkworm as well as the bee. Look at *Drosophila*, the fruit fly, without which the biological laboratories would be seriously handicapped in their studies of genetics.

The mongoose was imported into Jamaica to kill rats and snakes. It killed them, and along with them every unprotected chicken and other small animal on the island.

The Park Service eliminated mountain lions in the west. As a result bears multiplied until they became a nuisance, if not a menace.

Rabbits were thought admirable for Australia. On the contrary, Australia was admirable for rabbits. By a curious twist of ecology, no natural enemies were to be found there. The hares ate man's vegetables, the sheep's grass, and then began gnawing tree bark, and so exterminating Australia's few forests.

When the motor displaced the horse, the English sparrow population suffered an appalling decline.

The draining of marshes in the American north has killed more ducks than all the hunters' guns.

When the Tennessee Valley Authority proposed to build reservoirs forty miles long, malaria snapped back into the picture after fifty years of steady decline. Unless something was done and done correctly, these great lakes would become a paradise for malaria-spreading mosquitoes. (Something is being done, but it is a skilled and costly undertaking.)

Caspian Bookkeeping

The most monumental attempt ever made by man to improve his conditions while maintaining the balance of nature is Russia's program for her eastern rivers. It is primarily a problem in Caspian Sea bookkeeping. Ilin describes it as follows. It is more than a plan, for work has started and trucks are rumbling through Russia labeled "Sverd-Volga Construction."

It is proposed to take a large amount of water from the Volga for irrigation and for industrial and city-water supplies. Dams are to be built impounding large lakes. Lakes mean increased evaporation and more water loss. The level of the Caspian Sea under this condition must fall, for it is a landlocked sea no longer connected with the ocean. When an ancient upheaval cut it off from the Black Sea, it fell seventy-five feet before a balance was struck.

Its water income now consists of entering rivers, chiefly

the Volga, and the rain and snow which fall on its surface. Its outgo consists of evaporation. The Volga contributes 270 cubic kilometers of water a year, which would fill a barrel as big as Moscow and as tall as Mt. Kazbek (16,000 feet). Other rivers contribute 90 cubic kilometers; rain and snow, 450. This 810 cubic kilometers of water income all evaporates and comes down as rain on the Caucasus and the steppes. Without it these regions would turn to desert.

Oceans have a common account book, but the Caspian must do its reckoning alone. If Volga water is diverted, the Caspian level will fall and disaster will begin. Navigation on the sea will suffer; the fish industry—most important to Russia—will decline; water will retreat miles from its present shore line, leaving ports, towns and industries high and dry. The climate will change; all South Russia will become hotter and drier, for it is largely the Caspian which now protects the Volga valley, the Don steppes and the Ukraine from the deserts east of the sea. "What we improve with one hand, we destroy with the other."

Obviously this was a terrible set of books; it could not be allowed to happen. The Academy of Science summoned hundreds of experts to the problem, to the tangle of problems: marine bookkeeping, fisheries, Karabugaz Bay chemicals, climate, dams, reservoirs, soil, wheat. There were kilometers of maps, charts, drawings and figures. Finally the planning conference came to a conclusion, and you have already guessed it—*the water level of the Caspian must remain unaltered*. If the Volga is to lose water for agricultural and industrial development, it must get water from somewhere else.

Where shall the Volga secure additional water? In its northern courses, it runs close to the Pechora and three other rivers which drain into the Arctic Ocean. The Arctic is not fussy about its level. By a series of dams, reservoirs and canals, these rivers are to be tapped and part of their flow turned into the Volga. A huge reservoir will shoot water either north to the Arctic or south to the Caspian. A man throws a switch and eastern Europe reverses its drainage system. Magnificent conception! But the book-keepers found that this was not enough water for the Caspian. So they proposed to tap the Don River too. The Volga and the Don are not far separated at one point, and a canal will join them, a canal with locks, of course. Here water will be shot east to the Caspian or west to the Black Sea, into which the Don empties. Boats and barges will go from the Volga to the ocean through this canal—a vision of which the czars used to dream. Observe how essential in the planning is a huge amount of hydroelectric power.

But can the Don spare the water? How about its book-keeping? Fisheries, navigation, water supply for cities and irrigation are now all dependent on the Don. Yes, the Don can spare some water. Its annual income is twenty-two cubic kilometers; its outgo is eight. It can give the Volga an average of fourteen cubic kilometers. The project involves another great reservoir which will furnish power and irrigation for the Kalmik steppes and help to control floods on the Don. In the terrible flood of 1926 the river rose fifty feet. But just a moment. If too much Don water is diverted to the Caspian, the shellfish in the Sea of Azov at its mouth will die; they need a specified mixture of fresh and salt water. So the experts thoughtfully allowed a quota of Don water to the lobsters and the clams.

All this makes the Tennessee Valley Authority look like a kindergarten exercise. One cannot help wondering if the Academy of Science has thought of everything. This is land and water planning on a cosmic scale. Will something break loose? Will the books keep in balance? Whether the project succeeds or fails is another story, one which history will be at some pains to record, for there has never been anything like it in the world before. All that I wish to emphasize here is the matter of interrelation and inter-dependence. The Russians at least know what nature demands and have tried to deal faithfully with her—down to the very oysters in the Sea of Azov. Observe, they have not sought to bring back the primeval environment. No. They have accepted both industrial civilization and nature and have tried to reconcile the two. In America we have accepted the one and flouted the other.

Chapter V

THE GREAT WHEEL

CASPIAN Sea bookkeeping raises the question of the water cycle. Water comes down. How does it get up? Plants, as we saw in the last chapter, can be grown without soil, but not without water. All vegetation contains water, like the human body, to the amount of 95 per cent. It takes 1,000 pounds of moisture, on the average, to produce one pound of food. Nothing is more important in this study than to trace and understand the ways of water. Fortunately scientists have worked out the matter in great detail. They call the story:

The Hydrologic Cycle

The author of *Ecclesiastes* was wise before the scientist: "All the rivers run into the sea, yet the sea is not full; unto the place from whence the rivers come, thither they return again." The Great Wheel turns. A culture to be secure must be placed where soils are fertile and water is abundant. Sun and air, save in machine-age cities, take care of themselves.

The total water on the planet is believed to be a fixed

69

quantity. The planetary books show a constant capital. But the capital runs perpetually through the following great arc:

1. Sun and air suck up moisture from oceans, lakes, rivers and green leaves, and suspend it in the atmosphere. Oceans and lakes *evaporate* moisture; leaves *transpire* it. Transpiration takes place after the plant has absorbed water through its roots, and is thus a kind of internal process, while evaporation is an external one. A spruce forest transpires as much as 8.5 inches of water annually. Meanwhile, evaporation alone has been known to lower a reservoir eight feet in a year. Remember the Caspian Sea.

2. The moisture-laden air moves upward. When it cools or strikes a cooler body of air, the vapor condenses into tangible drops and down it comes as rain, snow or hail. Also it may settle more gently as fog or dew. About eighty per cent of the water vapor in the air condenses into rain or snow, and is called *effective precipitation*.

3. When precipitation strikes the earth, the first part of the rainfall is absorbed by the surface. When the surface is well soaked, more water goes into underground reservoirs by the process of *infiltration*. When the rate of rainfall is greater than the rate of absorption plus infiltration, the surplus runs off through rills, brooks and rivers.

4. The rivers carry the runoff back to the ocean for subsequent evaporation.

5. Meanwhile the underground reservoirs slowly release their stores into springs, marshes, streams, to be carried away later. They deliver much to the long roots of plants to help them over the dry seasons.

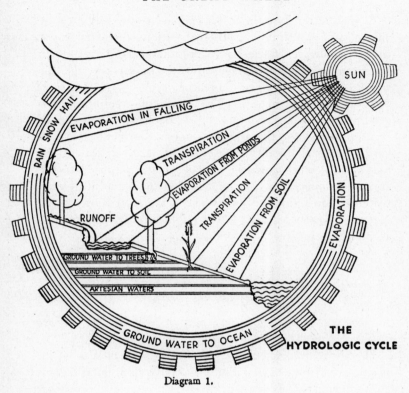

Diagram 1.

6. Plants transpire the water they have absorbed into the air again. Transpiration is the exhalation of watery vapor from the surface of the leaves or other parts of plants in connection with the passage of water or sap through the tissues. It is the way plants breathe.

Wheels within wheels. The ratios of precipitation to absorption to infiltration to runoff to transpiration cannot be determined for the world or for a continent, for they vary with each locality. Observe that a good deal of the rain which comes down in a given area is returned to the air almost immediately, never reaching the sea at all. Ocean waters are in the nature of reserve accounts. Following the National Resources Board, we might prepare a specimen account for the area X as follows:

	Per Cent
Ground evaporation	20
Infiltration to storage underground	30
Infiltration immediately used by plants and transpired later	25
Runoff	25
Total effective precipitation	100

Here is hydrologic bookkeeping for the state of Wisconsin, as prepared by Governor Philip LaFollette's Regional Planning Committee. Wisconsin receives an average precipitation of thirty-one inches of water from rain and snow during the year, the equivalent of ninety million acre-feet. Thirty per cent, or twenty-seven million acre-feet, runs out of the state, and not even the Supreme Court can stop it. Two-thirds of this goes to the Mississippi, one-third to the Great Lakes. "During its transit it serves in the generation of hydroelectric power, in the removal of human and industrial

72

sewage, in some instances for drinking purposes. A fourth
use of the runoff is in erosion whereby the earth is reduced
to a bare peneplain. The checking of this erosion presents
to the citizens of Wisconsin one of their great conservation
problems." Subtracting twenty-seven million acre-feet from
the ninety million acre-feet of rainfall leaves some sixty-
three million acre-feet to go into the Wisconsin soil. Most
of it does not stay there long. "Available studies indicate
that in a normal year most of the rainfall received in the
growing season returns to the atmosphere through direct
surface evaporation and transpiration through vegetation
growth." It is estimated that forty-five million acre-feet is
evaporated and transpired during the growing season. This
leaves eighteen million acre-feet to remain on the ground,
in lakes, marshes and surface waters, or to filter through the
ground into deep artesian basins. In summary:

	Millions of Acre-feet	Per Cent
Runoff.	27	30
Evaporation and transpiration.	45	50
Storage, surface and underground. . .	18	20
Total Wisconsin rainfall.	90	100

There is nothing man can do about the larger aspects of the
hydrologic cycle. Water will go up, and it will come down.
Under natural conditions life adjusts itself admirably to this
majestic wheel. Man creates mischief by changing the ratios
between runoff, infiltration and evaporation. This he does

whenever he shifts the earth cover from forest and grass to tilled land. Take the critical region just west of the 100th meridian. Here the shift from grass to corn, wheat and other crops has reduced infiltration and increased transpiration and runoff to such an extent that underground storage has dropped twenty feet and more in the past few years. Without storage, ponds and streams go dry; the whole aspect of the region begins to change for the worse. An acre of corn in its growing season transpires 3,000 tons of water, the equivalent of fifteen inches of rainfall.

Rainfall is not so much the determining factor as is the *balance* between rainfall and evaporation. Twenty inches of rain produces fine forests in Canada, while in certain areas in Mexico it produces fine deserts. Forests tend to occur, according to Sears, when rainfall is greater on the average than evaporation. Grasslands tend to occur when evaporation is greater than rainfall by a small margin. If the margin grows beyond a certain point, deserts form. These laws of the hydrologic cycle have been available for some time, but American farming has paid no attention to them.

Rain Makers

Some forty years ago, had you been living in a certain district in Texas, you would have thought that the Mexican War and the Civil War had been jointly revived. The air was full of shells, hundreds of pounds of explosives were detonated, 475 bombs were set off, 68 balloons blew themselves to shreds with oxyhydrogen gas. Little boys shrieked with delight. Presently down came masses of debris and a

74

few drops of rain. In 1926 a huge electric charge from a high tower in Los Angeles gathered clouds and a small drizzle. In 1931 Russian scientists employing war smoke screens on a tremendous scale were rewarded with eight minutes of rainfall, and later succeeded in stopping rain over a small area.

Man can tamper with the hydrologic cycle at the rain-making stage, but so far purely as a laboratory stunt. It is like obtaining energy from the atom, which can be done, though it costs a million times as much energy as it releases. It is doubtful whether the rain makers will ever produce a practical method. Suppose that they did—and duly patented it under the name of General Weathers, Inc. What pretty problems this would raise in a competitive world! On the one hand, travel bureaus, summer hotels, railroads, steam-ship lines, air lines, automobile manufacturers, the makers of bicycles, kodaks, bathing suits and Easter parade ensembles, proprietors of baseball clubs and the American Lawn Tennis Association—bidding high for fine weather. On the other hand, farmers, coal companies, cough-cure manufacturers, undertakers, and makers of raincoats, umbrellas, furs, woolen goods, skis, sleds and tire chains—ready to pay heavily for rain and snow!

The Primeval Balance

Let us try to envisage the Great Wheel as it rotates. Most of the factors involved have been touched upon in the discussion of the hydrologic cycle and in the preceding chapters, but it is helpful, I believe, to bring them all together in their dynamic relations. The factors are many and the interrelations are far flung and complicated, but we can at least convince ourselves that the wheel moves to change our lives.

Four main considerations are involved:

1. The primeval balance.
2. The assaults by man on that balance.
3. The temporary gains secured by these assaults, in terms of higher living standards.
4. The boomerangs: how man has assaulted himself or his children and grandchildren.

The primeval balance may be illustrated in a general way by the accompanying chart. The factors here shown, working one with another, produce natural life at its maximum— what was defined in Chapter II as "climax."

The sun operates the hydrologic cycle, drawing water from the earth and depositing it again.

The sun controls temperature and climate according to latitude.

Sun, wind, water and ice break up the minerals of the rocks to form soil.

Rain irrigates the soil and allows plant life to begin.

Plant life nourishes animal life, on both land and water.

Plants and animals manufacture mineral deposits over long ages—coal, oil, phosphates.

Forest and grass areas expand.

Rain infiltrates through soil to form artesian basins as storage reservoirs.

Rain gathers into lakes, swamps and marshes to form surface reservoirs.

The reservoirs nourish the season of scarce rainfall, and so limit droughts.

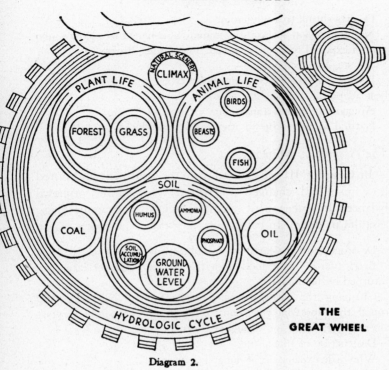

Diagram 2.

77

Deserts shrink to a minimum.

Natural erosion shrinks to a minimum, confined to a slow sculpture of exposed rock and some cutting of river banks.

Soil steadily accumulates.

Forest and grass reach their climax crops; the finest species, the best adapted.

Animal life reaches a maximum vitality.

Natural scenery achieves its greatest splendor.

The Assault by Man

In Chapter III we cruised over the continent and noted how man had changed and often wrecked the primeval balance. In subsequent chapters we shall examine these assaults in detail. In broad summary they comprise:

Destruction of the earth cover and with it the soil.

Extraction of plant food from the soil at a greater rate than returned by fertilizers.

Changing the ratios between infiltration, transpiration and runoff, thus upsetting the balance of the waters. Natural reservoirs are reduced; floods and droughts are encouraged.

Destruction of animal life.

Wholesale exhaustion of mineral deposits.

Much destruction was due to ignorance of the hydrologic cycle and its laws, and much was due to recklessness and greed. It was assumed that the resources of the continent were inexhaustible simply because they had not yet been exhausted.

Furthermore, as nature lost, man gained for a time. Up to the close of the nineteenth century the gains were so considerable that the nation felt a false security. The assets of the period should really stand on the books as deferred charges. They include:

A greater supply of foodstuffs than the primeval environment afforded. New crop lands from forest and grass and from irrigating arid lands.

A far greater supply of raw materials, especially from mineral deposits and from timber.

More available energy, by virtue of mining coal, oil and natural gas and damming rivers.

A great improvement in the means of transport: waterway, railway and highway.

An accelerating tempo in living standards—at the cost of declining resources.

Boomerangs

The list of boomerangs already returned is much longer, and when we add those which will return in the next few years, "if present trends are projected unaltered into the future," it will be longer still. Man has suffered and will suffer more from unnatural drought, dust storms, low-water stages, flood, erosion, silting, pollution and the invasion of salt water into crop lands; from forest and prairie fire; from an unnatural increase in pests and insects; from increasing costs of lumber, fish foods and furs; from exhaustion of grazing lands and mineral deposits; from the spiritual effect of ugliness and desolation.

Already America is pockmarked with blighted areas which leave their inhabitants no choice but to migrate or go on the dole. Above and beyond the economic loss is the fact that millions of Americans have come to call these

79

communities home. This is the place where they live; their roots are here. A thousand associations hold them. America is not a mine to be exhausted; it is a homeland to be cherished. No other interpretation is admissible. Statistics of production piled column on column are irrelevant. If raw production is all that our country is good for, we had better go to live in Mexico, where the good earth is respected, put on overalls in the morning, climb into an airplane and commute to gashed and smoking Ducktowns so long as they last.

I know of no more poignant illustration of this point than the following letter from the wife of a farmer in the stricken lands of western Oklahoma:*

Wearing our shade hats, with handkerchiefs tied over our faces and vaseline in our nostrils, we have been trying to rescue our home from the accumulations of wind-blown dust which penetrates wherever air can go. It is an almost hopeless task, for there is rarely a day when at some time the dust clouds do not roll over. Visibility approaches zero and everything is covered again with a silt-like deposit which may vary in depth from a film to actual ripples on the kitchen floor. . . . A good many people have left this country temporarily or permanently. . . . In these families there have been two deaths from dust pneumonia. Others in the neighborhood were ill at the time. . . . On a sixty-mile motor trip yesterday we saw many pitiful reminders of broken hopes and apparently wasted effort. Little abandoned homes where people had drilled deep wells for the precious water, had set trees and vines, built reservoirs, and fenced in gardens—with everything now walled in or half buried by banks of drifted soil—told a pitiful story of loss and disappointment. I grieved especially for one lonely plum

* Caroline A. Henderson: *Letters from the Dust Bowl. Atlantic Monthly,* May, 1936.

thicket buried to the tops of the twigs. . . . Naturally you will wonder why we stay where conditions are so extremely disheartening. Why not pick up and leave as so many others have done? It is a fair question but a hard one to answer. . . . I cannot act or feel or think as if the experiences of our twenty-seven years of life together had never been. And they are all bound up with the little corner to which we have given our continued and united efforts. To leave voluntarily—to break all these closely knit ties for the sake of a possibly greater comfort elsewhere—seems like defaulting in our task. We may *have* to leave. We can't hold out indefinitely without some return from the land, some source of income however small. But I think I can never go willingly or without pain that as yet seems unendurable.

Chapter VI

CROP LANDS

How They Have Stimulated Erosion

OUR airplane survey finds the continent of North America increasingly restless under the assaults of the white-faced animal upon its surface. Here and there swift and terrible reprisals have been taken. More are indicated. Is this survey overhasty and too alarmist? As it stands, it might justly be so interpreted. Let us come down from the heights and inspect the situation on the ground, armed with the latest documentary findings and with such a rare and competent study as *Little Waters*.*

It has been difficult to plan the chapters which are to follow because of the chain of causes and effects which I have called the *Great Wheel*. One cannot isolate any aspect of the cycle. Land, waters and wild life are all part of one organic whole. One must be a kind of whirling dervish to tell the story, or a mathematician dealing in five or six

---

* *Little Waters, Their Use and Relations to the Land*, by H. S. Person with the cooperation of E. Johnston Coil and Robert T. Beall, for the Soil Conservation Service, Resettlement Administration, Rural Electrification Administration.

dimensions simultaneously. A plain author using common language can simply do his best.

Here is a sloping cellar door. Take a watering can and sprinkle a quart of water on the top of the door. Measure the amount which slides off. Except for a little evaporation, the whole quart will be at the bottom, and it gets there almost instantly. Now tack a piece of thick carpet on the door; to cement it on would be still better. Fill the can and pour a quart of water on the top of the carpet. Your measuring trough at the bottom will be lucky if it receives the merest trickle at the beginning. Observe that the trickle continues for a long time as the water slowly filters through the mat.

This is the story of erosion in its simplest form. The cellar door is any land with a slope; the canful of water is rainfall; the bare boards are bare fields, or fields cultivated between the crop rows with the rows running down the slope; the carpet is natural cover, either grass or forest. In the first case, most of the water comes down, dissolving the top soil and taking it along. In the second case, the cover absorbs the water, puts much of it into ground storage, to be slowly released. Almost no soil comes down. Broadly speaking, American agriculture is a bare cellar door without any carpet on it.

When we admire the fantastic sculptured peaks of the Yosemite, or the Grand Canyon of the Colorado, we are admiring geological erosion. This is the kind that cannot be helped. Ice ages are erosive processes. When river banks crumbled in spring freshets in 1630, it was part of the natural order of things. In this discussion we are interested only in unnatural erosion, the kind produced by man, and we shall use the term in that meaning.

American soil vitality suffers from three plagues: erosion, depletion through cropping, and leaching—all man made. Experts are in some disagreement as to whether depletion is worse than erosion or vice versa, but they agree that both are disastrous. In erosion, both plant food in the form of mineral matter and the earth itself slides downhill. In depletion, only the minerals come out, largely incorporated in the body of the crop, and are shipped away to market. They can be brought back by artificial fertilizers, but usually are not. Leaching is the dissolving of minerals in rain water and the carrying of plant food out of the topsoil underground. It occurs on bare crop land and can happen when fields are level. It also is a serious source of loss.

Water erosion, unlike wind erosion, cannot of course take place on dead flat land. It is estimated by the National Resources Board that eighty per cent of the surface of America is sloping. That offers plenty of scope. How steep must the slope be? Unless one has studied the matter, one will be surprised at the mildness of the gradient which will lose soil. I have a dirt tennis court built to drain to the west with a four-inch difference in level over a standard width of sixty feet, making the slope 1 to 180. To the eye the court is flat as a griddle. Yet after a heavy downpour I have dug as much as fifty pounds of surface clay out of the wooden drain chute.

Tennis courts are more subject to erosion than crop lands because they are packed harder and offer little absorption

ERODED HILLSIDE IN TENNESSEE VALLEY
Before erosion control work undertaken, September 24, 1934.

SAME HILLSIDE TWO MONTHS LATER
Erosion control work carried out

PLATE IV.—Eroded hillside: before and after control.
(*Photo by T.V.A. staff.*)

for the rain. But crop lands are often steeper. In Tennessee I have seen cornfields where, if one missed one's footing, one would land in the next county. Some gradients by actual measurement are over eighty per cent. The erosive power of water varies in geometric proportion with its velocity. When the slope doubles, erosion quadruples. Traditional American practice has encouraged erosion by:

Plowing oversteep slopes. Slopes more than twenty per cent normally belong in forest. Slopes between ten and twenty per cent normally belong in grass. In some cases five per cent is the limit for tillage. (My tennis court is less than one per cent.)

Failure to rotate and diversify crops. One-crop farming, generally speaking, has been a curse to soil fertility. The pioneer with his diversified agriculture was far easier on the land.

A selection of commercial crops like cotton, corn, tobacco, which require cultivation (weed elimination) between the rows, thus allowing water a fine smooth channel in which to operate.

Plowing rows up and down hill against the natural contours of the land, thus starting gullies for the water to finish.

Leaving fields bare after harvest instead of planting a grass or grain cover. This practically assures a tennis-court surface, and water can tumble down anywhere it pleases.

When rain descends on natural cover, it percolates through the duff and litter and down through wormholes and other tiny openings into ground storage (granting of course that enough rain descends). Now take the same rainfall on the same area after crop land has replaced natural cover. Again it runs into little holes and begins to percolate into storage. The holes are there. But the water and the moving particles of earth form a *film*, a thin cement, and *close the pores of the*

85

soil. Subsequent water cannot get through into the A horizon (the topsoil) and down the slope it goes. It used to be thought that the litter absorbed the rain and prevented runoff. Dr. W. C. Lowdermilk of the Soil Conservation Service produces exhaustive evidence to show otherwise. The litter does absorb some rain to be sure, but the effect is secondary. The main effect of the forest or grass carpet is to keep rain water *clean.* On plowed ground the water muddies at once and soon the earth pores close. Then the rain, shut off from percolation, goes rushing downhill.

The first effect is *sheet* erosion. This is a general skinning of the rich topsoil under the momentum of the water, so insidious that it passes unnoticed. In time the farmer finds his yield per acre declining as plant food is being washed away. Sheet erosion is the most serious, though not the most dramatic, form of soil wastage today. It can be measured but it cannot be seen.

After sheet erosion comes *finger* or *shoestring* erosion. This is visible. It is as though one let one's fingers drift through the soil down the slope in an elaborate system of tiny wandering furrows. It marks the beginning of grave danger.

After the fingers come the *gullies.* One furrow becomes a main channel. The others feed into it like twigs into a branch. It cuts deeper and deeper and as it goes down it cuts back. It grows like compound interest. We shall presently inspect a gully 200 feet deep, covering 3,000 acres. When a gully system goes far enough it is practically incurable.

With hard work and great patience, the area *may* be brought back to grass or forest, but not for centuries to

CROP LANDS

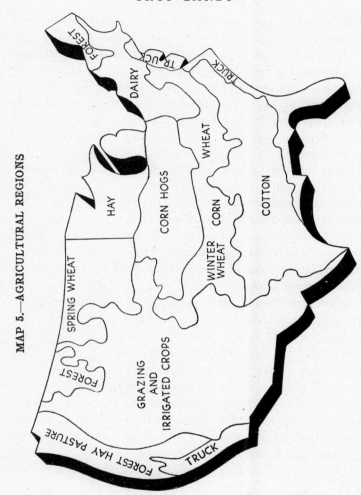

MAP 5.—AGRICULTURAL REGIONS

87

tilled crops. In many cases it must remain permanent tumbled desert.

Erosion is an earth disease, and it spreads. In Ducktown the disease has been fatal. By way of contrast, here are the Marshall silt loam series of soils in Missouri. Natural cover anchors them. In the past 1,000 years soil scientists calculate that they have been subjected to a percolation of water equivalent to a column. 1,700 feet high. And they have stood firm.

Here are two adjacent fields of Kaffir corn in Kansas. On (1) the soil is bare between the rows as usual. On (2) grass has been sown between the rows, which is highly unusual. (1) lost 4,250 times as much soil as (2) in a measured period, and its water runoff was 399 times as great.* Three hundred and ninety-nine times: imagine what this means in stimulating floods in the rivers below! The Forest Service studied three adjacent plots in the Appalachian forest. In the first, the forest litter remained in natural condition. Its runoff was taken as 1. In the second, the litter was burned off. The runoff promptly increased to 10. In the third, the litter was raked off for four successive years. The runoff shot to 160. The Soil Conservation Service, measuring land in Georgia, found that on a five per cent slope topsoil twelve inches thick, if plowed and left uncovered, would disappear in twenty-five years. If forested, the same land would hold its top soil for 35,000 years—not allowing for soil building from decaying vegetation.

On a steep Kentucky cornfield, a pouring thunderstorm

* Robert Marshall: *The People's Forest.* Harrison Smith & Robert Haas, Inc., 1933.

will "let loose 100 to 400 tons of water per acre per hour. After two or three crops the land is through." The National Resources Board reports that, by and large, on the same slope, grass is 65 times as effective in preventing erosion as clean tilled crops and absorbs five times as much water. The board has also prepared an impressive annual balance sheet of estimated national soil losses. The "losses" are from erosion, depletion and leaching. The "gains" are from fertilizers, manures, nitrogen fixation by legume crops and natural soil building. All figures are in tons.

	Losses	Gains	Net loss
Organic matter, total	322,000,000	100,000,000	222,000,000
Nitrogen	16,100,000	11,800,000	4,300,000
Phosphorus	2,500,000	1,100,000	1,400,000
Potassium	36,200,000	4,800,000	31,400,000
Calcium	53,600,000	13,800,000	39,800,000
Magnesium	16,800,000	4,600,000	12,200,000
Sulphur	11,300,000	8,700,000	2,600,000

This study is based on a billion acres of farm land, including crop land, pasture and woodland pasture. Carrying net annual losses into the future, the mathematical calculation shows that all organic matter will be gone in 136 years, a shorter time than the republic has already existed. This is one of those curves which never happen in fact, because the process either quickens or moderates its pace, but it well betrays the trend.

Take the matter of the return to the soil from commercial fertilizers alone. H. H. Bennett, head of the Soil Conservation Service, estimates the loss of plant-food minerals due to erosion at forty-three million tons a year, while the National Fertilizer Association reports some 670,000 tons of such minerals spread on the fields of the country for the year 1934. "In other words, erosion is sweeping off 65 times as much plant nutrients as are contained in the commercial fertilizers applied to our lands."

According to the State Planning Commission of Arkansas, three million acres of good bottom land in the state has been "irreparably destroyed" by stones, gravels and sands washed down from the fields above. This is an important point. Observe that erosion first takes the topsoil, which may or may not benefit farmers below. Sometimes it does. (This raises a nice point as to the law of property.) But when the gullies have cut through the topsoil into the B and C horizons, then nothing but tons of debris come down, ruining the neighbors' fields. Debris comes down faster than soil. The B and C horizons absorb less moisture than the topsoil, for there is less air in them and they are heavier. So runoff increases relatively as the cut wears deeper. Erosion becomes from two to four times as great, according to measured studies. Farmers in Bedford County, Virginia recently protested a reservoir in the headwaters on the very frank plea that their lands had been increasing in value because of silt washed down from above. "They feel that one of their vested rights is impaired if they are to be deprived of further enriching themselves at the expense of the upper counties." These farmers are due for a rude awakening. Wait until the topsoil is gone and hardpan and gravel begin to slide, at two to four times the rate!

Seventeen million acres of good Arkansas crop land has been gashed to the point where cultivation is no longer possible. On certain measured areas, a foot of topsoil has been lost in the last thirty years. Forest fires, according to careful studies, may increase runoff eighty-five fold. Arkansas is a dangerous state. It has many steep slopes. It specializes in clean cultivated cotton. Its rainfall is heavy and its winters are open, with little snow, so that the washing season lasts a full twelve months. There is altogether too much land in crops for prevailing soil types and topography. Erosion gallops. One-quarter of the crop land, according to the commission, should be retired to forest or grass. Large farmers can afford to rotate their crops and they do better. Small farmers are forced to cultivate intensively and are in a terrible plight. The figures for farm tenancy in Arkansas bear out this conclusion.

New Mexico reports overgrazing as the chief cause of its extensive erosion. Other hundreds of thousands of acres have been ruined by cultivating land not suited to crops. An investment of $25,000,000 in dams and irrigation projects in the state is now seriously threatened by silt. Pennsylvania reports half the topsoil of the state lost in a century of farming. South Dakota finds nitrogen content down, capacity to hold water failing, water and wind erosion increasing cumulatively. From the Washington wheat district comes the statement, "If wheat farming is continued, this land will become worthless." Dr. Arthur E. Morgan of the TVA reports that in 100 years erosion has destroyed one-half the good farm land of the Tennessee Valley, which is one reason why cornfields have been forced up the steeper

91

slopes. Iowa is perhaps the most fertile area in the union, if not in the world; once largely covered with tall flowering prairie grass, only about one-tenth of the state today has escaped some degree of erosion. "Since the cover was first disturbed, Iowa has lost approximately 550,000 tons of good surface soil per square mile, or a total of thirty billion tons." Forty per cent of the state has lost from 50 to 75 per cent of its surface soil. Iowa lakes are filling with silt. "If these lakes are to be preserved for recreational purposes, an elaborate dredging program will have to be instituted."

The above figures are taken from the special report of the National Resources Board on State Planning Commissions. The reader may be confused by the differences shown. Sometimes grass holds back five times as much water as crop land, sometimes 399 times as much. The reason for the wide differences is variation in the sites chosen for the experiments. The steepness of the slope, the kind of grass, the kind of crop, the kind of soil, the volume of rainfall, the time of rainfall, the condition of forest litter—all act to modify final results. Note, however, that all results, everywhere, show runoff halted and absorbed by natural cover as against tilled ground.

STEWART COUNTY

When one becomes erosion conscious, a motor trip through the country, especially west of the Alleghenies and south of Washington, D. C., becomes an endless game of finding gullies. One spots them as a beggar spots a coin. As the traveler scans the surrounding fields, he frequently loses sight of some classical examples just off the shoulder of the highway. In spanning the nation with concrete roads, erosion has been forgotten, and both highways and adjoining farm lands are suffering in consequence. The smooth concrete gives the water an admirable start for gouging a side ditch down the hill. Some of this damage has been repaired. In Oklahoma one finds neat check dams beside the highways; in Tennessee under the TVA, wild roses among other cover crops hold the highway cuts and fills in place.

In pursuit of this grim game, I once followed gullies to their supreme exhibit in this country—Stewart County, Georgia. Ducktown's nemesis was chemical, Stewart County's is purely mechanical; no smelters have speeded up the process. The county is halfway down Georgia on the Alabama line in the midst of the cotton belt. The topography is rolling but there are no mountains or even considerable hills. The soil is, or used to be, excellent. We drove in from Americus, over a blood-red dirt road, past cotton fields awaiting the plow in March, groves of long-leafed pine, shacks that passed for farmhouses, bleak unpainted churches, jessamine vines, evil side gullies, a lovely square red-brick courthouse, mules, happy-go-lucky negroes, broken down Fords, deserted lumber mills, rickety cotton gins, crossroads stores whose whole stock seemed to be Coca-Cola and chewing tobacco.

The road ran due west to the Alabama line. Suddenly across a dipping valley we saw the hill on the other side laid open in a bright red scar 50 feet wide. "That's one of 'em," said our driver, "but not the best one. You wait." It was evident that he took a certain pride in the exhibits. We passed without stopping a vast red cavity on our right. Gashes and declivities now became common on either hand.

Presently the road approached a kind of isthmus, perhaps 100 yards wide. A plowed field was on the left and beyond it a sickening void. A battered church stood on the right, a few pines about it, then another void. "Yes sir," said our guide, "Here's the old he one, the one on the left. He started the whole system. And do you know what started him? A trickle of water running off a farmer's barn about forty years ago. Just one damn little trickle, and now a third of the county's gone—forty thousand acres. Don't get too close to the edge. Sometimes she goes in, an acre at a time."

"Where is the barn?" I asked.

He pointed his thumb to the center of the earth. "Yes, the barn, the farm, a schoolhouse, a church, a graveyard, other farms—all gone. You see this road with a gully on each side? Well, they've moved the road three or four times already, but this is the last time. Come summer and a few smart storms, and the field here will go, that church will go and the gullies will join and there'll be no more road. And how will you get to Alabama then?"

"I suppose you'll have to go around," I said.

"Yes sir, you will—at least ten miles either side before you hit solid ground. There's nothing but nests of gullies north and south. This was the last way through."

We got out of the car and approached the brink. Only once before have I seen a comparable phenomenon—the canyon of the Yellowstone in Wyoming. That was geological erosion, and even grander; this was manmade, but sufficiently superb. The land fell away almost sheer for 200 feet. We stood over one of the gully's arms and far down caught a glimpse of the central basin. Shaped like an octopus, it covered more than 3,000 acres. A red gash on a little hill a mile away marked the tip of another tentacle of the same gully. (You saw its picture in the Frontispiece.)

The chasm was awful and beautiful. The earth strata changed from red to yellow to brown, mauve, lavender, jade, ocher, orange and chalk white. Pinnacles rose from the gully floor, sometimes with a solitary pine tree on their top at the level of the old land, banded and frescoed with color. Along the banks, trees were in all stages of collapse—some just ready to plunge downward, some holding on by their roots with might and main, some leaning crazily outward. At the bottom, a few small pine trees were alive and growing. Sometimes one lived with its red sod about it halfway down the slope where it had fallen. There was no water at the bottom. When the rains came, soil and water rushed off through a vent to the Chattahoochee River.

It was something like looking into the crater of a volcano, only instead of eruption one feared a cave-in. The good earth had given up the struggle. Now and then as we started a boulder would detach itself from a side wall and fall with a sickening crash into the abyss. Yet here was a field plowed right to the edge.

"I reckon his cotton will go down," said our guide.

"Can this whole thing be stopped?" I asked.

"Yes, I think we could stop it. We could never bring the land back of course. But if we went up on the height of land and diverted every drop of water, and then planted the bottoms and sides where they weren't too steep with kudzu vine and black locust, we might stop 'em. It would cost something."

"What ought to be done with them?"

"Well, sir, I'd have the government buy up the whole county and turn it into a national park—with plenty of railings. You might even charge admission. You don't see a sight like this often."

I looked into the vivid, slipping horror.

"No," I said. "You don't."

The technique of controlling erosion is still being worked out. Our guide indicated one of the methods. Local conditions dictate the remedy to be employed, but broadly speaking there are seven chief methods.

Return of natural cover. Steep slopes to be taken out of crops forever and planted with trees; less steep slopes to be planted to grass and held permanently as pasture.

Rotation of crops. Instead of planting corn every year, a given field will be sowed to corn the first year, to a grain crop the second year, to clover the third and back to corn the fourth. The clover fixes nitrogen and is plowed in to enrich the soil.

Terracing. This consists of scooping broad embankments along the contour lines of a tilled field to catch the rain water. The terraces are some rods apart and are connected by a down channel, preferably cemented or stone lined, to carry off surplus water without harm.

Contour plowing. This gives the effect of many little parallel terraces and is a less expensive job.

Strip cropping. Leaving broad strips of grass or nontilled crops along the contour lines between the plowed land. These act as field-wide dams.

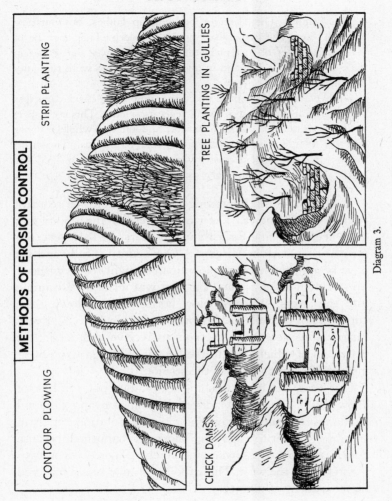

METHODS OF EROSION CONTROL

STRIP PLANTING

TREE PLANTING IN GULLIES

CONTOUR PLOWING

CHECK DAMS

Diagram 3.

Check dams. These are for building up gullies, but must be applied before the gashes have worn too deep. They may be of concrete, lumber or just plain trash. The runaway soil settles in back of each small dam and in due time, if all goes well, the gully fills in.

Gully planting. Advanced practice is now using check dams less and hardy, creeping, fast-growing vegetation more. This is cheaper, as it passes the job back to nature, and on the whole is more effective. It is biological control rather than mechanical. The shrub masses spread a tangled cover over the wounded earth, hold the water and begin to rebuild the soil.

Techniques are improving daily, but erosion control itself is hardly news. The rice growers of the Philippines have been terracing for a thousand years. In 1813 Jefferson wrote of his farm in Virginia: "Our county is hilly and we have been in the habit of plowing in straight rows, whether up or down hill . . . and our soil was all rapidly running into the rivers. We now plow horizontally, following the curvature of the hills and hollows on dead level. . . . Every furrow thus acts as a reservoir to receive and retain the water, all of which goes to the benefit of the growing plant instead of running off into the stream."

Our land has been washing away, but not for lack of knowledge. Jefferson, Madison, Washington and Edmund Ruffin were practising contour plowing, rotation and strip cropping a century ago and more. It happened because Americans as a class were indifferent. There was always virgin land to the west. Three thousand miles was considered the equivalent of infinity.

Stewart County has gone. No work by man or nature can

bring it back within a calculable future. Tens of millions of acres of American crop lands are taking the same precipitous path, and no virgin west remains. But all over the country groups of men like the conservation worker who drove us to Stewart County—lean, tanned men with clever hands and keen eyes—have set to work to check the landslide. Many farmers are aiding them. But they cannot do it alone. There must be more of them, and they must feel the force of public opinion behind them.

Morris L. Cooke, sometime chairman of the National Resources Board, sums it up:

Just as with bodily diseases such as cancer or tuberculosis which can be cured only in the early stages, so it is with soils built up through the ages. Once ravished beyond a certain point, they are incapable of restoration except by nature's slow processes, which are measured not in tens, but in thousands of years. Leaving out all 'if's, and's and but's,' running the risk of being precise in an area where precision may have no place, I believe that at our present rate of soil erosion, this country of ours has left to it less than a century of virile existence. . . . We have two decades at the most to plan our campaign.

Chapter VII

GRASS LANDS AND THE DUST BOWL

THE primeval continent was half forest land and almost half grass land. The latter included the sturdy tall and short native grasses of the prairies and the Great Plains and the assorted cover of arid lands and natural meadows. Certain areas of parklike forest, especially in the south, combined trees and grass. Grass has had few poets and fewer scientists.* We have foresters but no "graziers"—to coin a word. When forest goes, everyone can see it go. When grass goes, the effect is less dramatic, but equally important. In this chapter we shall dedicate a song to the grasses of America.

As I looked about me I felt that the grass was the country, as the water is the sea. The red of the grass made all the great prairie the color of winestains or of certain seaweeds when they are first washed up. And there was so much motion in it; the whole country seemed, somehow, to be running.†

---

* Walt Whitman's *Leaves of Grass* has a fine long poem about the redwood trees of California, but only a few scattered lines about grass itself.

† Willa Cather: *My Antonia*. Houghton, Mifflin Company.

When the price of meat goes up, we berate the packers. But this, observes Paul Sears, may be only the result of declining grass. Year in, year out, under natural conditions, the yield of grass is sure; planted fields are never sure. Crops are speculative equities; native grasses are predepression government bonds. Hardly any native grasses now remain on American farms. Eastern pasture grasses are imported, not native. Two specialists recently had to travel 30,000 miles back and forth across the Mississippi basin to find satisfactory specimens of vanishing species. "The prairie sod is on the way to join the dodo."

Any motorist knows what grass means to the land—if he stops to think a moment. Let him try to turn his car in a sand lot as against a lawn, or even a patch of wild beach grass. No golfer need be told the difference between a sand trap and a fairway for a firm shot and a firm stance. Dust storms are an awful warning that the earth has literally lost its roots. Man in America has moved from east to west. Dust storms blow from west to east.

Four hundred years ago Castenada came up from Mexico upon the Great Plains, with no end but a horizon. "Who would believe," he wrote, "that 1,000 horses and 500 of our cows and more than 5,000 rams and ewes and more than 1,500 friendly Indians and servants in traveling over these plains would leave no more trace where they had passed than if nothing had been there—nothing?" He felt the great quiet strength of the grass, as generations of settlers after him.

This recalls the miracle of Sweetwater Springs. Before 1850 travelers used to refer to the curious circumstance of

101

digging ice in July in the upper Sweetwater River in Wyoming. After that year people laughed at them. The heat of the
desert must have turned early travelers' heads. Ice in July
indeed! Hewitt in 1862 became very sarcastic about Delano's
account of the ice in '49. Both were conscientious reporters
and both were right. The explanation is simple. A little
side valley was fed by springs, near the covered-wagon trail.
In winter a small glacier formed. The tall thick grass made a
thatched roof above it and preserved it into the summer,
even as deep shady rocks hold ice in Kings Ravine in New
Hampshire. The altitude was high and the nights were cool.
"The great number of animals accompanying the Forty-
niners destroyed the grass in the Slough; later comers never
found it of sufficient height and thickness to perform the
old-time miracle."*

Cattle Country

Cattle made the first frontier and grass made cattle.† Beef,
pork and mutton were the only crops which, in a land
without roads, would take themselves to market. After
cattle came the plow. In 1700 the range lay on the outskirts
of the Virginia settlements, in 1750 on the headwaters of
the Potomac. Then it moved west to Kentucky, Ohio, the
Mississippi, the prairies, the Great Plains—an arc of feeding
animals a thousand miles long. The pioneers did not hew
their way through a forest wilderness. U. S. Route 1 led
from Massachusetts to New Jersey to Pennsylvania to the

* A. B. Hulbert: *Soil.* Yale University Press, 1930.
† Some of this historical material comes from a magnificent article in *Fortune Magazine*, November, 1935.

PLATE V.—GRASS. (*Photo by Charles Krutch.*)

Shenandoah to Kentucky to Illinois, and it was largely paved with native meadow grass along watercourses and valleys.

General Bradley came out on the plains in 1868: "It seemed that all the flocks and herds in the world could find ample pasturage on these unoccupied plains and the mountain slopes beyond." Again the American concept of infinity. The eye could see no end, and the mind leaped to the conclusion that there was no end.

In 1867 the first cow town was established at Abilene, Kansas, on the Kansas Pacific Railroad. In 1872 the buffalo abdicated, and the cow fell heir to his range. Shortly thereafter the plains Indians abdicated, which coincided with recovery after the panic of 1873 and the rise in the price of beef. In the '80's came the world boom in western beef. By 1882, $30,000,000 of Scotch and English capital had been invested in the cattle business. The Prairie Land and Cattle Company, a Scotch concern, ran 150,000 head in Colorado, New Mexico and Texas on 8,000 square miles of land. XIT ran 160,000 head on three million Texas acres. Theodore Roosevelt took a range in North Dakota. The cowboy came into his own. The western saga was born.

> It was in the year of eighty-three
> That A. J. Stinson hired me.
> He says, Young fellow, I want you to go
> And follow my herd to Mexico

Big fortunes were made in hard cash, and bigger ones on paper. Grass was their foundation, building more wealth than coal or oil. The plains began to fill. Nothing checked the concept of infinity; there was always grass beyond. Most

103

of the range was government owned, and the public domain was early considered a great grazing commons on which no control or regulation existed—a curious and unfortunate mixture of socialism and individualism. By 1885 the range was full and many areas were overstocked. Grass which carried comfortably one steer to forty acres was trying to carry three or four. The blizzards and intense cold of 1886 wiped out half the cattle population and relieved the pressure. Many great cattle companies went into bankruptcy. The boom was over, but presently steers were coming in again.

The early cattlemen, according to Sears, had some rudimentary ideas of conservation. They could not control their lands, however, for they had grazing rights rather than ownership. Like the great lumbering operations of the same epoch in which stumpage was bought rather than the land, we find, not a system of responsible ownership, but a concession device in its worst form. Lumber barons hacked, burned and moved on. The cattleman was responsible for living animals. He knew that grass and water had to be conserved, and he realized that an overstocked range ultimately killed the sod. Not having title to pasturage, he was exposed to the strong temptation to take his profit while he could get it. "Under the system of land allotments, any planned and provident economy became well-nigh impossible." Overstocking, tempered by blizzards and sagging markets, became chronic in the cowboy country.

Sheep and War

In the early nineties the sheep arrived, and with them bitter war between the sheepmen and cattlemen. I shall never

104

forget the look I saw on a cattle ranger's face, years later in
Wyoming, when news was brought that sheep had been
sighted up on the rim rock. His eyes went to the Winchester
on the wall and he completely forgot his guests. It was as if a
son had been kidnaped. There were few truces in this war.
Winchesters barked; saltpeter was scattered around waterholes; blue vitriol was sifted on the range. At Rock Springs,
Wyoming, 12,000 sheep were slaughtered by cowmen.
Flocks were waylaid and driven to be torn to pieces by
mountain lions around Cheyenne and Laramie. Lonely cattle
ranches were burned by the sheepmen. The Tewksbury-
Graham feud reached the proportions of civil war in the Salt
River country.

Over wide areas the sheep won out. It was a victory not
only at the expense of the longhorns and the whitefaces
but also at the expense of the grass. There were three reasons
why the sheep prevailed. Cows will not feed where sheep
have fed; the odor repels them, however hungry they may
be. Sheep drink less and can be watered by tank cars and
other artificial means. Remember we are in dry country.
Finally, and most important, sheep have cloven lips which
eat down to the growing bud. Grass, unlike most vegetation,
grows not at the tip but at the joint. Overgrazing by cattle
checks growth since the foliage is eaten off; sheep kill the
living nub.

So the sod of the plains went out, no one thinking beyond
his immediate advantage or his immediate vendetta. Winter
ranges down in level country were opened for summer grazing. Originally they were too dry in summer, and the grass
had a chance to rest. But dams were built to water cattle in

105

summer on the lower levels and the grass lost its vacation. Summer ranges high in the mountains were invaded by sheep, which tore out the young grass at the retreating edge of snow and cut the sod to ribbons with their sharp hooves. "Mountains turned to caving bluffs of dust." Willows beside streams were eaten back to the stumps. Plum trees died. Sagebrush, the harbinger of a failing range, came in. Purple iris, which indicates that the upland grass is sick, made the mountains beautiful. The Yellowstone River, which had astonished Lewis and Clark with its clarity, ran dirty yellow. Acres blew to hardpan around the Texas waterholes.

The Last Destroyer

Then appeared the last and worst destroyer—the plow. It came with the railroads—C. M. & St. P., C. & N. W., U. P., C. B. & Q., "those unforgettable initials which meant more to the west than all the full-spelled names of history." West of the rainfall line at the 100th meridian plows had made little impression to the turn of the century. The standard gift of the government—160 acres to the home-steader—was too small for farming. Beyond the meridian it took 1,000 acres to support a family, and 1,000 acres was not to be had free. In 1909 the Enlarged Homestead Act increased entry from 160 acres to 320 acres; in 1916 Congress increased it again to 640 acres, a full section. The railroads, assisted by the Department of Agriculture, advertised the wonders of dry farming on the plains. The population of the Dakotas jumped from 14,000 to 510,000 in two decades. Between 1910 and 1920 North Dakota put ten million acres under the plow. Nature helped: 1914, 1915 and 1916

106

were well-watered years. The war helped: it brought high prices for wheat. The plow came in and behind the plow came settlers, speculators, traders, moneylenders and rising land prices. Cattlemen gave ground to farmers as the plow destroyed the winter range on the flat lands. Soon the herds in the high summer ranges had nowhere to go when the autumn snows came down. The balance between summer and winter range was again upset. Cattlemen turned their six shooters on the plowmen as they had earlier turned them on the sheepmen. They tried to frighten off the home-steaders, then to buy them off. Both methods were expensive.

To the overexpansion of the livestock industry, the disastrous wars between sheep and cattlemen, overgrazing and gradual reduction in the carrying capacity of the range, was added a last great blow . . . the coming of the homesteader and the resulting break-up of much of the range.*

The destiny of the short-grass country is pasture, except for crops in the river bottoms, if the land is to endure. But after a few years of good rainfall, out come the appealing dry-farming circulars, the speculators, the mortgages, the bright hopes and the homesteaders. Then the rainfall cycle swings to the dry arc and the farm goes off in a whirlwind. Thousands lose everything they owned but other thousands replace them.

The Machine

A team of horses and a plow can rip the sod, but a tractor drawing a battery of plows can rip it twenty times as fast.

* National Resources Board.

A wet cycle and war prices gave tremendous impetus to dry farming by power machinery. Panhandle cattlemen sold their herds and went in for wheat with great gang plows on the flat, loose and friable soil. Yields per acre were low but costs were lower still. The success magazines ran stories of giant factory farms. The doom of the little man was freely predicted—but the doom of the big man came first. The wet cycle turned to dry in the early '20's and the combines rotted like buffalo bones on the plains. Presently dust came and covered them. Factory farms may be on the books of the future but not in lands which nature sets specifically aside for pasture.

The advance of the Germans in 1918 cut seriously into the food supply of the Allies. Mr. Hoover as Food Administrator was worried. The first plan was to send Tom Campbell, the giant wheat farm expert, to the old Roman wheat lands in North Africa. Mr. Campbell preferred to feed the Allies from the Great Plains. He picked 600,000 acres on an Indian reservation, and in addition was given a ten-year franchise to farm any lands he pleased on ten million acres in Wyoming and Montana, at a rental of ten per cent of his wheat in kind, delivered at the railhead. The government would lend him no capital but J. P. Morgan and Company advanced $2,000,000.

Campbell has been called the most portentous plower of plains in the history of the world. For wheat he cared little, for grass less, but machines absorbed him. See them come: tractors, binders, threshers, combines, trucks, drills, disks, using 5,000 gallons of gasoline a day! The first summer he broke out 7,000 acres of virgin sod; two years later, 50,000.

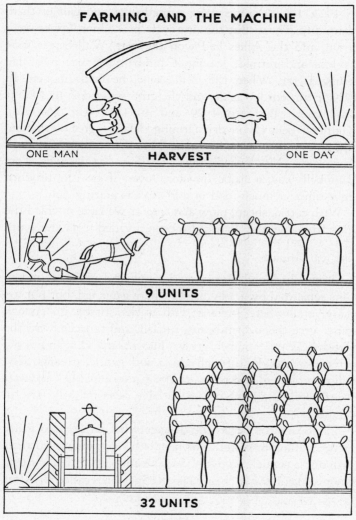

Diagram 4.

In 1923, 100,000 acres were turned over and half of them planted to wheat. But the dry cycle broke him. Prices were down, and the Allies had won the war. Wall Street took its loss and retired, leaving Campbell his machines. He struggled on. When the rains came, he made money. In 1929 it turned dry again and the crop was poor; in 1930 it was worse. Between 1929 and 1934 he lost $600,000. Campbell believes in dry farming. Many agree with him. But nine million acres are gone forever in wind erosion on the plains. "It looks," says *Fortune*, "as though Tom Campbell was a major disaster—even if he can produce eight times as much food *in wet years* as grazing can."

With cattle, sheep, plow and tractor we have invaded the grass from the east. It has also been invaded from the south.

The Rio Grande

Originally New Mexico was a semiarid region of mountains separated by grassy plains where game fed, but not too many, and where Indians with sticks stirred up enough soil to give them corn, beans, squash, and tobacco.* On the plateaus a little timber grew. The scanty rain and snow percolated slowly through pools and gentle streams. The region protected and renewed itself interminably. Today it is a desert. The Pueblo Indians have been its only faithful defenders.

The Spaniards began the debacle with cattle—too many cattle, trailing to water. The next shower transformed their path into a runnel. Soon it became an authentic gully, cutting down and cutting back: *arroyo*, the Spaniards called it. After

* Erna Fergusson, in the *Yale Review*, winter 1935–1936.

the grass goes, cattle eat the foliage of trees and brush, then the seeds. Roots are exposed, trees and brush die, and no seeds remain to restore them to life. Cattle cut down the stream banks and the little rivers spread to marshes. Then the wagons come, carving deeper ruts and bigger arroyos. Many famous old southwest wagon trails are now gulfs in the ground. Spaniards as well as Americans "pursued if they did not formulate the policy of taking out of the country more than they could replace."

The valley of the Chama River was once magnificent— red sandstone cliffs, cedar and piñon trees, fine fishing streams, pine forests up the canyons. The trees in the head-waters were leveled; the grass perished from overgrazing. The valley is now a desolation, gashed with gully erosion. Silt threatens the great government dam at El Vado. Below Abiquiu, farm lands once rich are today silt and sand waste below the ruins of fine old haciendas and chapels. Near Española erosion is at its peak. Only two side streams remain. The rest of the country has been carved by wind and water into the fantastic Santa Fé marl—bright colors, weird forms, "useless as the mountains of the moon." Nothing remains on which man can subsist. Towns and pueblos like Nambé, once surrounded by pasture, field and orchard, stand dry and desolate on the banks of empty stream beds. La Ventana, which originally supported a hundred prosperous families, now consists of three shacks.

In 1827 Mexico had 240,000 sheep on the tax rolls on New Mexico, twice the number now supported. The Rio Puerco was then a fine clear stream. In the dry season it is a crack in the desert. Between Santa Fé and Albuquerque on the Rio

Grande the country was irrigated by the Spaniards and for a time it bloomed. In 1880 the farm area was 125,000 acres; in 1926 it had declined to 45,000 acres. Silt constantly raises the river level and the irrigated fields turn into alkali swamps, Utopias for mosquitoes. Fields removed in flood from one side of the Rio Grande are delivered a soaking sandbar on the other side. Many villages have been completely washed away and even Albuquerque is threatened.

Elephant Butte Dam was built by the United States to guarantee New Mexico's quota of water "forever." Men who forget nature should not write such foolish contracts. "Forever" will end in a few years if the Rio Puerco, which chiefly ravishes the Rio Grande, is not controlled. Every flood season it pours 9,000 acre-feet of silt into Elephant Lake. Meanwhile the river bed, propped on silt, rises higher than the surrounding country.

The Sequence

Cattle invaded the grass where buffalo had long grazed. The grass and buffalo thrived together. But the steers were too many. They checked the vitality of the grass; their paths became gullies; they gave the range no rest. Sheep—too many sheep—cut to the heart of the grass with their sharp mouths and killed it outright. Forests in the head waters of the canyons were cut down. Plows ripped the sod loose all over the Great Plains. Huge areas were burned over to expose minerals or "improve" the range. Some authorities believe that fire was the most destructive of all the enemies of the grass. The plants of the virgin sod are mostly perennials. They depend less on seed for spreading than on new buds.

112

This gives them great flexibility. Both fire and overgrazing destroy the equilibrium.

When grass goes, erosion begins. No less than 165 million acres of grass now stand utterly devastated or seriously depleted. The great dust storms of recent years are not a chance phenomenon but the culmination of a long tragic process. After a storm, the fine silt scattered over the fields is impenetrable to water. Even heavy rains promptly run off. That is why rain in the Dust Bowl, which looks like a god-send, often means so little. Sometimes a single storm will remove several inches of soil, first the loam and fine sand, then the coarse sand. Finally the wind may take all soil down to hardpan and so create true desert conditions. Sand dunes begin to roll as on a beach. Good land beyond is covered by the marching dunes. What the wind leaves the water takes.

Dust is charged with electricity. It has been known to explode grain elevators. It strangles men and animals with dust pneumonia. It is a black menace to the aviation industry. Storms are now measured in terms of visibility. On good days one can see perhaps a mile, on poor days one block. Children are lost in these storms as in winter blizzards. Dust is more terrible than flood, a slow, pervasive horror. In late February of 1936 red snow fell in New England. It meant that the Dust Bowl was stirring again.

Dust storms are now news. For a long time the idiotic maxim, "It will hurt business," kept them quiet. They were muffled as Los Angles tries to muffle her earthquakes, with disastrous effects on life and land. "When the young editor of the Dalhart *Texan*," says *Fortune*, "finally decided

in the summer of 1933 to tell his readers that the sand
dunes they used for necking parties and picnics were crawl-
ing tides which might destroy the city, he lost $1,000 worth
of advertising in a week."

Dust blows in Russia too. The desert has been marching
on Bokhara. When the black clouds rise from Central
Asia, hundreds of miles away in Samara, the peasants say,
"The Persians are shaking their robes." Around Bokhara
the country was once virgin steppe. Sheep tore up the
turf. Saxaul trees were cut down for fuel and cactus bushes
were fed to camels. Now waves of sand sometimes forty
feet high are moving west, burying roads, fields, houses.
Walls are built against them as against an invading army,
but the sand overwhelms the walls. After a storm thousands
of fruit trees die. The Caspian Sea is the last barrier. Without this sea, as we have seen, all of South Russia would be a
desert. But dust gets through into the Volga region, where
droughts are becoming more frequent. The black-earth
region was seriously damaged by landlords in the nineteenth
century. The best manager was the one who stripped the
largest area of its natural cover.

Today the Russians are launching a vast campaign to
halt the desert. Sand can be held by the little kandym
plant. Its seeds are in a small round nut, covered with
bristles. The wind sends the nut jumping along the ground
and sand cannot catch and bury it. A little shrub starts.
The dunes grow fast but the plant grows faster. Soon the
dune is turned into a hillock of vegetation and ceases to
move. Kandym halts the desert and turns the victory over
to better grasses. The road to climax begins again. Seeds

are being sown by airplane. Modern Russians know what grass means.

Some Americans know. Sears tells the story of the Sand Hills of Nebraska. It is a cheerful story to compare with the gloomy ones which have gone before. This region comprises eleven million acres, a larger district than the agricultural lands of Egypt. Billowing grass-covered hills lie in a vast rock bowl which holds the meager rainfall and slowly passes it through the soil. In summer, when pastures to the east are parched, these hills are green and fresh. Due warning was given by a few great blowouts, funnel-shaped craters where turf had been removed. Nature tried to repair them with creeping Redfield's grass.

These hills were first God's and the buffaloes', then public domain. They were leased according to the usual custom as cattle range. There were many small lakes with lush meadows about them to be cut for winter feed. It was ideal cattle country if over-grazing could be avoided. Moses Kincaid was elected to Congress to give this kingdom to the people in homesteads one mile square—640 acres. He passed his law and in poured the settlers. A family cannot live by grazing 640 acres; much more is required. So the turf was broken by the plow; the hay meadows were wiped out. Some wheat was grown but presently the sand came bursting through. In the uplands the wind swirled against the crops and the abrasive sand cut them to shreds. In 1920 Sears found a family slowly starving on 640 acres, which in the Nile supports a thousand people. No milk, no butter, no eggs, no meat.

The Kincaiders retreated, discouraged and beaten. They

115

were fine pioneers, good workers, but they did not understand grass. The cattlemen returned—this time as owners,
for they bought the land from the vanquished home-
steaders. Herds are now being kept down to the carrying
capacity of the range. Slowly the turf is being brought
back. The lakes are filling again. The Sand Hills are green
once more.

Stockmen generally, according to the National Resources
Board, are coming to realize that only the withdrawal of
lands from homestead entry and the establishment of federal
control over the range will save the livestock industry.
Private management has been a disastrous failure. The
Taylor Grazing Act of 1934 is the real beginning of such
control. It authorizes the withdrawal of eighty million acres
of the public domain, to be organized into districts by the
Department of the Interior, with full provision against
overgrazing.

It takes a long time to bring back the grass. Overgrazing
often encourages poisonous weeds, as well as cactus and
thorns. The plant cycle must be worked through before
the good grasses return. But given a long enough rest, they
do return. Sometimes it takes buffalo grass twenty years
to recapture plowed land that has gone to dust. The Russian
thistle, which can initiate growth in dust-storm areas, is
being used here as well as in Russia.

There are many methods to check and control the march
of dust. Government scientists are constantly finding more.
But in the end there is only one real control: bring back the
grass. The margin of control is not large—only the length

of the roots, which alone can hold the outposts of our productive lands. In critical areas this means a margin of twelve to eighteen inches. As in the case of water erosion, control is beginning, but dust clouds roll even faster than floods. The fight will not be won until the people of the Great Plains rise in mass, with the rest of us behind them.

Dust is no respecter of property. The fight against it must be collective, not individual. One field that is not checked may start a whole township to blowing. In Kansas, county commissioners now list (plow deep) blowing fields and charge the cost to the land owner. Owing to the depression many farmers cannot afford gasoline to list their land—yet delay is fatal when blowing gets under way. A poorly tilled field, moreover, when its soil begins to go, can infect an adjoining field, even though the latter has been deep plowed. Modern highways, elevated above the plain to provide deep drainage ditches, are also serious infection centers; for there is nothing to stop the sweep of wind across them. Thirty counties in southwestern Kansas in 1936 voluntarily agreed to take one-quarter of the area out of wheat and sow it to the original cover—buffalo grass. This is better than any listing.

Jack Lambrey, a lonely sheep herder in Texas, is speaking: "It's a screwy life. But anyway, you get the open air. You get time to get acquainted with yourself. You get to use the grass. And grass is what counts. It's what saves us all— far as we get saved. Men and towns and such as that, don't amount to a particular damn nohow. Grass does. Grass is what holds the earth together."*

* Quoted by C. M. Wilson in *Harper's Magazine*, February, 1936.

Chapter VIII

FOREST LANDS

A FRIEND of mine lived in the Michigan lumber country as a boy. The industry, moving west, had reached the lake states. White pine was being followed as the Spanish once followed gold. Michigan had the finest virgin pine in North America; many trees shot up clear of boughs for sixty feet. Axes flashed and down they came like wheat before a combine, and nothing grew up. There was no second growth at all, just stumps and fire.

In the town where my friend lived there were seventeen lumber mills going day and night. Slabs and sawdust presented a growing problem. Some of the slabs were fine eight-foot sticks of timber. My friend's father was a minister and also owned an icehouse. He got his sawdust free. Slabs were given away. Citizens had special furnaces to burn nothing but slabs. Every one burned them furiously, but it made no impression on the supply. So they built a special kiln with stacks seventy-five feet high and rushed the slabs out from the mills on a conveyor. The kiln smoked and flared and puffed, devouring ten cords of slabs at a mouthful, but the mills kept far ahead of it. Then they took the surplus out and dumped it in huge pyres in the open fields. Flames roared to the sky. There was no night in the town. A pyre would burn for two or three years.

Suddenly the mills closed. The pines were all cut down. The mill workers were thrown on the streets. The town began to die. The town was based on wood, was made entirely of wood—wooden houses, wooden sidewalks, wooden streets paved with cedar blocks, wooden every-thing. Somebody carelessly threw a match in a pile of shav-ings. The wind was right, as it frequently is in Michigan. The town was consumed within an hour. People had to hurry. My friend lost everything he owned. Later he returned to the ruins and could not find even the site of his father's house. The tall pines had gone and man went faster. This was better, perhaps, than living in a dead town.

It is easy to become sentimental about trees. It is easy for me, when I remember the Brook Trail on Mt. Chocorua. But as Sears points out, a tree is not a museum. Trees are for the use of man. What is the best use?

A tree crop should be harvested when ripe even as a corn crop. Unlike the corn, however, trees do not all ripen at the same time. A proper harvesting selects the mature crop and allows the immature a chance to grow and ripen in its turn. Then the forest goes on forever and yields forever. The Forest Service cuts millions of acres of government lands on this basis. Only the ripe trees are taken. Seed pines are carefully left. Trees are felled to do the least damage to younger growth. The slash is piled and burned in wet weather. The forest is as healthy as it was before, sometimes healthier. This is the way trees are harvested in Sweden, Germany and other European countries. In Denmark there are now twice as many trees as there were seventy-five years ago.

Typical American practice has been very different. Forests have been leveled clean, the old folks, the strong adults and the children together. The strong ones have been taken off to the mills, and the rest have lain on the ground in dreadful confusion until the inevitable fire has come along and burned them up. After the fire the scar might be so deep that nothing would grow again, or a scraggly second growth of an inferior species might come up. When pine goes out, poor hardwood often comes in. The result has been that the cream of the forest has been skimmed. The Forest Service is seriously handicapped because so much of its charge is blue milk.

Many forests were also grazing lands with rich grass under the trees. The grass was often burned—"swingeing" they call it in Tennessee—in the mistaken notion that it helped the pasturage. Too many cattle ate away the undergrowth; seedlings, small trees, the children, were killed. The grazing forest became a kind of old folks' home. When the old folks died, there was no more forest.

The best thing that ever happened to the American forest was the depression. The total cut fell from thirty-seven billion board feet in 1929 to ten billion in 1932. The trees had a chance to rest. It was like a shattered army reforming when the enemy runs out of artillery shells.

Heavy Artillery

See how the artillery had grown. The first water-power mill in America was built in Berwick, Maine, in 1631. It operated a vertical saw blade and could handle only small-sized lumber. Big timbers had to be adzed by hand. The best that these vertical blades could do was about 1,000 board feet a day. The little water mill also ground grain, fulled cloth and ground plaster, powder, malt, flaxseed, mustard and tobacco. In 1767 the gang saw was introduced. It could cut 5,000 feet a day. In 1820 came the circular saw, and output jumped to 40,000 feet. The steam mill in 1830 raised daily output to 125,000 feet. In 1890 the band saw revolutionized mill operations. In the Pacific states a single mill can now cut a million feet a day.

In the early period men chopped pine trees about the water mill and brought the lumber in by hand. As the trees retreated, oxen were used to skid the logs. Paul Bunyan in the famous legend had an ox named Babe. When Babe drank the stream went dry; when he snorted the mill caved in. Logs were run down the rivers to the mills in booms and rafts. Horses replaced oxen as the sources moved back, and then the narrow-gage railroad replaced horses. Now huge tractors and overhead timber trestles—a kind of forest conveyor belt—have replaced railroads in the largest operations.

Thus methods for mowing down the forest have improved with marvelous rapidity. But methods to preserve the forest so that people might have something to use in the future, while well known, have not been applied except by the Forest Service in recent years. Hundreds of expensive mills full of modern machinery have been left in the ravaged woods to rot with the stumps. As tramper and camper I have often found them in the scarred wilderness, with raspberry bushes growing out of the decaying sawdust.

Friend and Enemy

Trees were very important to the early settlers, both positively and negatively. They furnished shelter, fuel and, to a less extent, food. They harbored game. They were responsible for four colonial industries: lumber, shipbuilding, naval stores and potash. Charcoal was also essential for the smelting of iron.

On the other hand, the forest was a great impediment to agriculture. The prospective farmers first girdled the trees and killed them. The underbrush was burned, the land rudely plowed and a crop taken. Then the stumps were grubbed and the wood rolled into a pyre. This operation was massive and required the help of the neighbors, as in barn raisings. It was the origin of the term "log rolling"— you help with my stumps and I'll help with yours. Potash from the ashes was used for making soap. Labor was at a premium in the colonial days, and turning forest lands into crop lands required prodigious labor. So the forest was often regarded as a hostile thing, an enemy to be killed as expeditiously as possible. Whole mountain ranges were burned off, though no farm lands were to be found there. Campfires ran riot. The settlers watched the flames on the crest with the same composure with which they regarded a massacre of defenseless Indians. This attitude was not universal, of course, but it was strong enough to sweep the forest steadily westward, strong enough to overcome the positive attitude, which looked on trees as friends rather than enemies. The prevailing temper was men against trees, not men working with trees. This temper still survives. When American soldiers were in France in 1917, they were

sometimes ordered to cut down trees for military purposes.
It is recorded that the peasants stood aghast at the fury
with which the doughboys attacked the forest. They
could understand ruthless assaults on Germans but not
on trees. France passed through her pioneering age
thousands of years ago, and the attitude of hostility
had long since changed to one of solicitous regard for the
forest.

The American forest was devastated with two objectives
which should not be confused: the clearing of crop land,
and the methods of the lumber industry as such. The former
was a blind razing and burning. "The poor white literally
burned his way west from the pines of Carolina to the
black-jack cross timbers of Oklahoma and Texas." Fire
the forest, mine the soil until its richness is gone, and
move on. Turpentine was bled from the long-leafed pine
by the wasteful "boxing" method which soon killed the
tree. Never mind, there were more beyond. "People
never felt that they must face their surroundings with
any finality."

New Hampshire and Maine were lumber communities
before they were agricultural. The Piscataqua River in
1650 was the center of the colonial lumber trade. The royal
navy wanted masts, spars and naval stores—turpentine
and oils. It was not until 1700 that the naval stores industry
moved to the south.

White pine was the prize. It was followed relentlessly
from Maine to New York to Pennsylvania to Michigan to
Wisconsin to Minnesota. As white pine died, yellow pine
was tracked down with equal determination. The swath

123

ran from Virginia to Texas. Then Douglas fir was assaulted in the northwest with a new variety of high-powered devices. The great trees came down magnificently, crushing the life out of the younger forest. This warfare is still raging, but "if present trends remain unaltered," Douglas fir will go the way of white pine, leaving its place bare. Hardwoods were pursued from the northeast to the Great Lakes, then south down the Appalachians. To find anywhere east of the Mississippi today a stand of virgin forest is a rare experience.

Let us take the case of Wisconsin as typical. Forests once covered six-sevenths of the state, chiefly white pine and hemlock. The lumber industry in Wisconsin reached its peak in 1899, when 1,033 sawmills were cutting 3.4 billion feet a year, two-thirds of it pine. In 1932 only 113 mills were still operating, cutting a beggarly 14.2 million feet, less than one per cent of the peak production. Meanwhile the Wisconsin wood industries require about 430 million feet of raw material a year, thirty times the local cut. The state has destroyed a valuable resource within its own boundaries and must now import raw material from the dwindling resources of the Pacific states. Lumber is a heavy product, costly to transport. As trees were removed in Wisconsin, much land was put into farms on soil too poor for anything except forest. Agriculture gained nothing; the forest lost everything. The same thing happened in Iowa, of which twenty per cent was once forest on the thinner soils. The trees were cut down; the resulting farm land was very poor and promptly began to erode.

124

PLATE VI.—FIRE. (*Photo by Charles Krutch.*)

The Toll of Waste

The wastes of the forest industry have been frequently stated.* Here we shall give but a categorical summary.

Fire.—The average annual loss is about $75,000,000, resulting from 150,000 separate fires. Many, of course, are small brush fires. The Forest Service estimates that the timber destroyed each year—about two billion feet—would build a five-room house every 100 feet on both sides of the road from New York to Chicago. The effect might be worse than the conflagration, but the loss is real enough. Fire affects the future of the forest by killing the young trees. It hastens decay by leaving scars through which insects and disease enter. It creates an unendurable desolation which only Ducktown can exceed. Fire, by stripping the litter and humus, encourages erosion and flood. Policy up to 1900 was to let it burn. I well remember the acrid smoke and copper-colored sun when, as a boy in New England, I was told that Canada or Michigan was burning up. The great fires of 1910 in Idaho and Montana, with more than 100 persons killed, finally aroused the nation. Today, thanks to the Forest Service, the state services and the CCC camps, great holocausts are often prevented.

Wind.—After lumbering has been badly done, heavy winds uproot large trees, which carry smaller ones down with them. The streamlined tops of the primeval forest guarded against such blowdowns.

Wastes in the Industry.—These include loose practice

---

* For an excellent summary, see *The People's Forest* by Robert Marshall. Harrison Smith & Robert Haas, Inc., 1933.

in the woods and in the mill. It is estimated that more than one-third of the tree disappears in these two stages, and much could profitably be saved. Poor seasoning of timber, failure to use preservatives, the wrong use of wood, as in hewn ties, the premature cutting of second growth, especially pulpwood, and box cutting for turpentine all come under this head.

Overgrazing we have already mentioned.

Speeding erosion needs no further comment.

Speeding floods.

Diminishing rainfall—a matter of some debate.

From these several causes it is estimated that 850,000 forested acres are devastated, ruined for future use, every year.

The Forest Service has prepared the following balance sheet for 1928:

	Per Cent
Total wood removed	100
Waste in the woods	25
Waste in the mill	12
Decay in storage and service	20
Miscellaneous wastes	11
Total waste	68
Total wood utilized	32

Of this loss, it is estimated that twenty-five per cent is clearly preventable.

The annual drain before the depression was twenty-five billion cubic feet against a growth for all American forests of only six billion—about four to one. Softwood,

126

however, was going *eight* times as fast as it grew. The peak of the industry came around 1907. Since then production has been declining and prices have been rising. In a generation prices went from $15 to $85 per 1,000 board feet, a flaming danger signal that what was once abundant was becoming scarce. In the depression, of course, prices fell, but now they are picking up.

With a total reserve estimated at 1,700 billion board feet (Chapter III) and an annual cut of forty billion, dividing one by the other demonstrates mathematically that in little more than forty years the American lumber supply will be gone. One cannot be too definite, because the natural growth factor must be allowed for on a diminishing scale and because long before lumber disappears prices will be so high that it will be cheaper to import from Canada or Russia.

Forest Philosophy

The phrase has often been used to summarize American forest practice, but it is still apt: "Cut out and get out!" A forest, like a mine, was to be exhausted and abandoned. It was viewed as something dead rather than alive and growing. The vital relationship to the equilibrium of soil and water was almost totally ignored. In 1828 President John Quincy Adams set aside 30,000 acres of live oak in the Pensacola district as a reserve for the navy. Andrew Jackson, the bucko from the backwoods, reversed this act in short order and threw the acres open for general entry. Reserves indeed!

The original idea of the young republic, according to Silcox, was to convey forest ownership to individuals in small lots. Actually a man who entered a timber or stone or homestead claim on forest land could realize on it only by selling the stumpage to an operating lumber company. He could not crop it himself because big trees take organization to move to market. (It is a curious fact, however, that with all the advance in technique no one has yet invented a machine to chop down a tree more expeditiously than a man with an axe.) After the timber was felled and removed, the land might or might not be worth farming. If it could not be sold, the owner normally stopped paying taxes. Skinned of its value, it reverted to the public domain. Thus the government presented the alleged homesteader and the lumber company with a rich slice of continent, and in due time had the plate back licked clean. This was known as sturdy individualism, but to me, at least, it seems a very expensive kind of dole. The original policy was perverted to create a highly transitory and unstable lumber industry. The forest rather than being acquired for use, according to the intention of the founding fathers, was acquired for quick commercial profit.

When cut-over lands become tax delinquent, the tax base is narrowed and a heavier load falls on citizens who are really using their lands. Roads and schools must be maintained. Marginal farmers cannot pay the heavier taxes and they go under. The base shrinks and rates rise again. The next poorest group of farmers is forced out. "By this process of pyramiding," says Marshall, "it has actually happened that entire towns and almost entire counties have been abandoned because the chief taxpayers, the timber owners, have withdrawn their contribution to local government."

Here is Jackson County in the Lake Superior region.

128

When the lumbermen arrived with mills, railroads and stores and assailed the white pine, the county boomed. Farmers moved in to share the prosperity. The pine was annihilated and replaced with scrub, stumps, brush and fire. The ex-timberworkers cleared more land for farms. A big drainage project was undertaken, but the soil was too sandy and crops would not grow. Foreclosures were served right and left. Speculators went to the cities and promised fortunes on these "rich irrigated lands." The suckers swarmed out and took possession of the foreclosed farms. Presently they were sold out too. County taxes were not paid on the cut-over areas. The thrifty had to meet the additional burden. A study showed twenty poor families each paying $10 in taxes and receiving $185 each in roads, schools and other county services. Finally the whole county went into bankruptcy. The federal government is now buying up the land for national forest.

"Privately owned timber lands continue to be destruc-tively exploited, and local forest bankruptcy, stalking on the heels of boom conditions created by rapid liquidation of forest capital, has been and continues to be a drastic reality for hundreds of communities in the forest regions."*

When second growth is harvested before it is mature, "the result is a povertystricken industry operating spas-modically, and forcing operator after operator into loss of invested capital or bankruptcy."* Everybody loses in this game—continent, general public, county, farmer, forest worker, mill worker, and often the lumber company itself. It is true that fortunes were made in the peak years, like that

* National Resources Board.

of Weyerhauser, but generally speaking the lumber industry has been a long cascade of bankruptcies. Never was its condition worse than at the present time.

In these circumstances it is nonsense to expect hard-pressed operators to conserve their stumpage. They cannot afford to in most cases. Fast-growing tree crops in the south take forty years to mature; lodgepole pine in the Rockies takes 150 years. The lumberman as an individual thinks in terms of his own lifetime. Where will he be in 150 years? He takes what he can get—or tries to keep his loss to a minimum—and gets out. Trees grow slowly; money in the bank grows faster. "Forcing a lumber company to practice forestry [permanent-yield management] against its will is almost as futile as forcing a school boy with no musical sense to take piano lessons when he wants to play baseball."

The whole system is wrong. Despite a good policy on paper, it started wrong and has been getting progressively worse. It started under the American concept of infinity. "By the time the theory of forest inexhaustibility became clearly fallacious, lumbering methods were too deeply fused with capital investments and industrial competition to be changed overnight. Thus America's magnificent forests fell before an economic system which had no philosophy of conserving natural wealth, and it left in its wake millions of acres of land largely stripped of resources necessary for human habitation."* Almost 100 million acres now stand devastated, cleaned out, nonviable. More than 50 million acres are tax delinquent and the rate of delinquency grows.

* "American Conservation." The American Forestry Association, 1935

Six per cent of private woodlands—twenty-four million acres—is devoted to permanent-yield forestry; the other 94 per cent—376 million acres—is still operated on the cut-out-and-get-out theory—except in the case of farm woodlots. Meanwhile the government is practising forestry on 140 million acres of its own land and also controlling fires on a large fraction of all private lands. Theory and practice confirm the conclusion that, with a century-old crop like timber, the only owner who can be counted on to devise and carry out a long-time program of management is the government. Already the public owns almost 200 million acres of woodlands, about one-third of all. Western irrigation and water-power projects are largely dependent on national forest. The Forest Service estimates that, of 615 million acres in the country altogether, 308 million have a major influence on watershed protection and another 150 million have an important influence. Lumber, we must emphasize again, is only one part of the forest story.

Under continued private ownership and short-term management, the lumber industry and the forests can be expected to go from bad to worse. This resource, like an oil pool, is simply not susceptible to brittle concepts of property. Not even responsible individual ownership has been obtained, but rather an evil concession system. Three-quarters of the American forest is a vital element in land protection, and so an asset to every farmer, hydro-electric company, irrigation company, and city man, who, even if he does not drink water, demands it in his plumbing.

Is the forest a community charge or is it not? Suppose that we accept it as a community charge. Suppose that

the federal government and the states, with the Forest
Service as expert manager, take over the effective control,
if not the ownership, of the American protective and productive forest. What must be done to halt progressive degeneration, yet give a dependable lumber supply to perpetuity?
How long before the President of the United States will
be able to declare a national holiday because the curve of
annual growth has passed the curve of annual cut, and the
forest, after three centuries of tragic decline, begins to
build again?

Robert Marshall has prepared an estimate, based on
Forest Service figures. Of the 600 million acres of so-called
forest land, bring approximately 500 million under community control. He figures the cost at about a billion dollars.
Now let intensive forestry be practised on a part of this
domain, extensive (less rigorous) forestry on a larger part.
Let the balance be protected against fire and disease. By
1950 the yield should reach twenty-one billion cubic feet a
year. Predepression demand was somewhat less than that.
The curves would have crossed! The government, meanwhile, as forest manager, bent on conserving the supply,
would give every encouragement to the use of substitute
materials. Let us have houses of glass, chromium, aluminum,
corn shucks, brick or adobe. Every foot of lumber saved
helps to rebuild the forest.

No private company can follow such a course. Only the
community, following the long-term objectives of lumber for
industry and protection for land and water, can restore the
forests of America.

132

Chapter IX

UPSTREAM

THE rain falls on crop lands, grasslands, forest and those scarified and expanding areas where nothing grows, and begins its journey to the sea. As we saw in the account of the hydrologic cycle, part of the water goes back to the atmosphere through evaporation and the transpiration of plants—if plants are there; part goes into storage on the ground or deep underneath; the rest immediately begins to run off. The runoff gathers into rills, the rills into brooks, the brooks into streams, the streams into feeder rivers, the feeder rivers into main rivers.

When the runoff from a given rainfall ceases, the brooks and rivers continue to flow from the storage waters welling up in springs or held in lake, pond, marsh and swamp—unless man has emptied the natural reservoirs. The whole system of interlacing courses is commonly called a *watershed*,*

* Technically a *watershed* is a zone following the height of land that divides one drainage area from another—like the ridgepole of a house. Common parlance also calls the basin bounded by that zone a *watershed*. So does the second definition in the Oxford Dictionary. We shall use the word occasionally in the common connotation. It is a defter word than *drainage basin*, which sounds a little like something under the kitchen sink.

133

or, if we wish to be exact, a *drainage basin*. In this chapter and the next we shall trace the rainfall from the point on the height of land which divides one watershed from another, down the upland valleys and the lowland valleys to the ocean. We shall note the problems and conditions, one after another, which the water creates as it comes down. In a primeval environment there are conditions but no problems. When man comes in, the problems gather.

The real conservation problem of the west is the conservation of water. . . . From Nebraska west, water and water alone is the key to our future. We need the mountains and hills and great protected back country or we cannot have sufficient water for our valleys. . . . There must be a great western strategy for the protection of our watersheds and the plant life on them. . . . We must replace homestead thinking with watershed thinking.

In saying this, Secretary Wilbur emphasized the profound difference between the old point of view and the new. The old way was to secure a homestead from the public domain, treat it as exclusive private property and try to sell it, speculate with it, or secure a living from it. Little thought was given to the effect of the use, or misuse, on the neighbors or on the continent.

The new way is to think of a particular piece of property as set in the frame of the whole basin and to realize that, if the watershed area is seriously damaged, this property and most other properties will be worthless. Before tracing the rainfall down, let us make the situation concrete by telling the story of one actual basin—the Central Valley of California. Here is a definite problem which nature will settle if man does not. She will settle it decisively and disastrously for a very considerable population.

Central Valley

The Central Valley extends half the length and a quarter the width of the state of California. It is as long as the line from Cape Hatteras in North Carolina to New York City. The valley floor comprises 19,000 square miles, the whole basin 40,000 square miles. The elevation of the floor is low, seldom exceeding 500 feet. Down from the north comes the Sacramento River, up from the south the San Joaquin River. They meet in a tangle of swamplands and flow west to San Francisco Bay.

The valley with its two main rivers is a mountain-walled trough in which has accumulated the wash of centuries. Upon the rich soil has settled a large agricultural population, growing oranges, apricots, peaches, celery, rice, cantaloupes, prunes, pears, onions, asparagus, almonds, figs, olives, grapes and spinach. These products are farmed intensively by efficient modern methods. They are packed, branded and shipped all over the United States. The valley accounts for more than 50 per cent of the total national commercial production of many of these food specialties. It is one of the most productive and important agricultural districts, not only in America, but in the world.

Without irrigation the area would be blistering and arid, save for strips along the rivers. What water it gets comes mostly from the snows and rains of the mountains beyond.

In humid regions east of the 100th meridian, water is normally so abundant that it is taken for granted, like air. In the valley water is scarce and its value high. Politics, economics, law, life itself, revolve around this scarce and vital agent. By virtue of its use, millions of Americans outside the valley are fed with fruits, vegetables and grains. Great transportation and trading investments are involved in shipping and delivering the valley's output. Without water the valley ceases to be a place for human habitation, the foodstuffs disappear, the investments are worthless.

When settlers first came, they obtained water by diverting the rivers through irrigation ditches. Crops were abundant and profitable. As the valley grew and prospered, more water was diverted until the sources began to run low. Underground water was then pumped from the great artesian basins laid down by mountain snows. The pumps multiplied with the outgoing carloads of food. For years now the water table had been falling; the inflow from percolation is less than the outflow from pumping. Before long the pumps will have beaten the snow altogether, and the artesian basins will be exhausted.

Now let us follow the two rivers to their conflux in the delta. This is the richest soil of all, 400,000 acres of black muck. One cannot farm a swamp, and the region has been reclaimed by large and costly projects. But the reclamation work has caused the land to settle until now much of it is below sea level. Salt water from the Pacific creeps into the irrigation channels. It can be held back only by the pressure of fresh water from the rivers above. The rivers, or what

136

MAP 6.—CENTRAL VALLEY OF CALIFORNIA

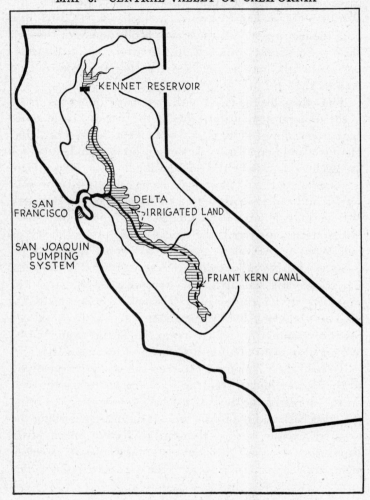

KENNET RESERVOIR

DELTA

SAN
FRANCISCO

IRRIGATED LAND

SAN JOAQUIN
PUMPING
SYSTEM

FRIANT KERN CANAL

irrigation has left of them, cannot supply the pressure. Without the swamps, moreover, which used to catch and hold the melting snows, the spring floods now race through clean-cut channels to the sea. In the latter part of the growing season the race is reversed: the Pacific comes in and poisons the land.

Thus the valley is faced with two major questions: How is the underground water table of the artesian basin to be kept from falling? How is salt to be kept out of the delta? Here is a large population dependent on land and water for its livelihood, calling the snow-walled valley home. Here is a huge agricultural investment, a long-established economy, settled and functioning, with a thousand complex ties with the world beyond the mountains. But unless these two questions are answered, the desert comes in and man goes out. What is the valley going to do? What is the nation going to do? No individual farmer can solve this problem. No conceivable calculations of pecuniary profit and loss can solve it, for this is not a business corporation but a place where people live. We are confronted with a matter of resource planning in which nature holds the trump cards. We are also confronted with a matter of life and death.

To hold the valley means to keep the water from rushing to the Pacific. But to keep the water means to stop erosion on the slopes of the Sierras, to check overgrazing, to bring the grass back and the forest back. It means replenishing the lowered artesian basins. It means collective effort, strict stipulations for land use, the end of speculative developments and very careful rules as to the use and reuse of water.

It means the building of reservoirs, and cheap power to pump water where it is needed.

From the engineering point of view, the problem is capable of solution. Competent reports have already been filed and some work already started. The Sacramento River has an excess of water at certain seasons which can be held by dams and fed to the San Joaquin Valley by pumping. In this way pressure can be maintained to control the salt of the delta. But the program, to succeed, calls for more collective action and responsibility than the people of the valley have ever undertaken. Will they adjust their property institutions and their individual wills to such engineering? Whether they will or not determines their future. The planning is thus not a matter of engineering alone; it is also a matter of human institutions, laws and habits.

The Water Hierarchy

The Central Valley illustrates certain problems, but there are many more. Any watershed area is concerned with some of the uses of water itemized in the following list. A big drainage basin, like the Mississippi or the Columbia, is concerned with all of them.

1. Water for drinking and domestic purposes.
2. Water for livestock.
3. A ground water level high enough to nourish crop roots.
4. Irrigation of arid lands.
5. Supplementary irrigation of humid lands in dry seasons.
6. Water for industries, factories, steam boilers, ice making.
7. Fisheries.

139

8. Water for game birds and wild life.
9. Hydroelectric power.
10. Navigation.
11. Recreation, swimming, camping, scenery.
12. River sites for cities and towns.
13. Rivers as political boundaries between states and nations.

The above are all uses of water. Here are the chief abuses:

1. Floods, artificially accelerated.
2. Low water artificially encouraged, the obverse of flood.
3. Pollution, human and industrial.
4. Erosion on the valley slopes and on river banks.
5. Silting and gravel wash.
6. Salt-water invasion at river mouth.
7. Destruction of fish, shellfish, bird and game life.
8. Destruction of natural reservoirs, ground and artesian.

A primeval river basin knows no abuses. A healthy watershed under human control should show uses at a maximum and abuses at a minimum. Perfection is too much to ask. Beginning our journey downstream, perhaps the first consideration is the matter of natural reservoirs, which keep brooks and rivers flowing. Remember that we are working within the Great Wheel where everything is interlocked, and separation of functions is difficult.

Natural Reservoirs

East of the 100th meridian the ruling principle has been to throw water out; west of the line the aim has been to coax it in. In the east we find large drainage projects to rid

140

swamps and marshes of water. In the west are large irrigation projects to flood arid lands and make them produce.

Near the meridian itself, trouble has been brewing for a
long time. Since the lands on this zone were settled, the
underground table in the Dakotas, Minnesota, Nebraska,
Iowa, has dropped eight to seventeen feet. Wells must go
deeper and deeper, plant roots reach farther, while springs,
ponds and lakes recede until many go dry. The rivers from
these regions find their water bank accounts steadily
shrinking. To make matters worse, the shrinkage accumulates from year to year, like compound interest. Devils Lake,
once the largest body of water in North Dakota, has been
dropping since 1900. By 1934 the lake had all but disappeared. A study by the Mississippi Valley Committee
in the dry season of 1934 showed springs generally weakened
in the Dakotas and dry in most counties. Ponds were
completely dry. Lakes were down two to eleven feet.
Streams were mostly dry, and rivers very low. In western
Iowa springs were weak and all ponds dry. Kansas and
Missouri reported their rivers the lowest in history. The
drought of 1936 has made the figures even worse.

Underground, the pressure of the great Dakota artesian
basin—which underlies parts of Minnesota and Nebraska
as well—owing to "careless drilling and finishing of wells,
to unlimited waste of water, and to failure to control old
wells, wild wells and leaks, has been rapidly depleted. Wells
have ceased to flow over large areas. Unless the waste is
checked, most of this area will cease to yield flowing water."
In the 100th meridian zone, says the Mississippi Valley
Committee, the change from grass to crop has reduced

141

infiltration and increased transpiration. This change plus waste of water has disastrously reduced both surface and artesian storage. In parts of South Dakota underground waters have dropped forty feet in twenty years. This all comes home to me, for as I write I can hear the grind of the electric pump which lifts water from my artesian well. Where would my household be if the well went dry?

The same thing has happened in the Central Valley of California, as we have already noted. Artesian waters often cover interstate areas. They contain many years of accumulated inflow. When they are depleted, it takes years to bring them back. Broadly speaking, depletion results more from poor use of land than from wells and pumping. Yet these basins are the ideal storage reservoirs. They cost nothing, for nature built them. They have no evaporation losses. They make it less urgent to flood valleys and move people for artificial reservoirs. Their regulation is perfect and automatic. When man disturbs their equilibrium, he begins to destroy the functioning of the whole watershed area.

Marshes and Swamps

Let us turn to the lands east of the 100th meridian. In these more humid areas, the problem is surplus rather than shortage, though a hasty plan will encourage shortage in due time. Much low land here was drained by speculators to promote the selling of farms to people who knew little about farming, much of it as an answer to a real demand for more crop land when markets for agricultural products were brisk. When marshes are drained, the result is often

142

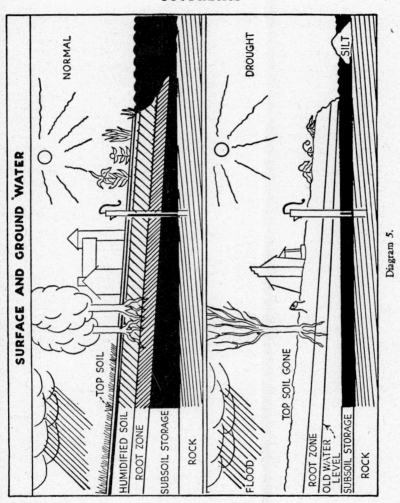

SURFACE AND GROUND WATER

NORMAL

DROUGHT

SILT

TOP SOIL

HUMIDIFIED SOIL

ROOT ZONE

SUBSOIL STORAGE

ROCK

FLOOD

TOP SOIL GONE

ROOT ZONE

OLD WATER LEVEL

SUBSOIL STORAGE

ROCK

Diagram 5.

143

inferior soil for farming. Left alone, marshes are a genuine resource as protectors of wild life, birds and fur-bearing animals; they are useful for hunting and recreation; they may be farmed for natural crops such as cranberries.

Consider the Great Swamp region of Wisconsin, as reported by the planning commission of the state. Early settlers cleared a little of it for damp hay lands. By 1890 the hay lands were being plowed in dry years. The first crops were fabulous. Agriculture started with a rush. But the marsh fertility did not last, and a series of wet years reduced the farmers to desperation. In 1894 action was taken to drain the Great Swamp in a thoroughgoing fashion and create an impressive new agricultural area. Nearly 800,000 acres was drained at a cost of $5,482,000. It was money thrown away. Two-thirds of the area turned out to be submarginal soil, useless for crops. Vast tracts degenerated into dry peat bog, subject to long, terrible, smouldering fires. The speculators had their happy days but the farmers, the state, the wild life and the watershed area—in this case the Wisconsin River—had only grievous losses. Now the federal government is spending money to restore the Great Swamp to swamp.

Central Wisconsin's man-made desert is being restored to its natural moist green under the Federal Works program. Thousands of acres of slough in farm counties were drained by real estate boomers many years ago, the new land being offered at bargain rates to settlers. But the hummocky acres would not grow crops. The present project calls for the building of 50 dams to return the land to its marshy state.*

* *New York Times*, Mar. 1, 1936.

This may be boondoggling, but nature appreciates it. The ground water level is being raised, the peat fires have been extinguished, the birds are nesting again, the forest is coming back, while sportsmen and recreation seekers have a new area to roam over.

The National Resources Board reports much speculative drainage of land in Florida as premature and ill-advised. The ice ages created a great glacial lake in Minnesota, known to geologists as Lake Agassiz. In due time it became a peat bog supporting a fine stand of timber. The forest was cut down. The stimulus of the war resulted in extensive drainage operations. Settlers swarmed in with plow and harrow but, as in Wisconsin, the soil was poor, the peat was ravaged by fires, and the settlers were left stranded.

Some of these swamp areas make excellent farm lands of course, but nobody, in the eagerness to take advantage of high prices, ever stops to consider what sections are good and what are bad. Promoters charge in and ruin the rich land with the poor. The conception of proper land use has escaped them altogether. Finally, we must not forget that in certain areas marshes are drained to keep mosquitoes under control. This however is for the health of man, not of nature.

There is such a thing as being too neat and tidy. Swamps are often dismal and rank. People itch to clean them up. Leave them alone, fellow citizens, leave them alone—unless a whole board of experts, as described by Mr. Ilin, should condemn them. Like grass, they help hold the world together.

Water Supply and Pollution

With storage considered, we now start down the river. Soon we find a little town in the upper courses which is using the stream for its water supply. Good. The water is clear and wholesome, unless the lands above are subject to erosion. The people of the town drink the water and use it for domestic purposes, the local tannery uses it, the creamery washes its cans with it, and a sewer outlet close to the town dump delivers it conscientiously back to the river—but with many interesting additions—interesting, that is, to the bacteriologist or the chemist. The oxygen in the stream goes bravely to work on the additions, and, depending on their volume and the amount of oxygen available, the out-come may or may not be happy.

We go on to the next town, and the next. Presently we are in a position to formulate what might be called the Law of Dumping Down. Town A takes clean water, drinks it, converts it into sewage and delivers it via the river to town B, which—sometimes—purifies it, drinks it, converts it into sewage and delivers it to town C, which drinks it, converts it into sewage and delivers it to town D—and so on down to town N.

A dozen towns in a row on the northern courses of the Mississippi express this law. According to the Mississippi Valley Committee, the Red River of the North—what a fine, bold name!—is a source of drinking water and waste disposal for Fargo, Wahpeton, Grand Forks and lesser cities. Yet rainfall and runoff are such that in low water the river is an open sewer and in cold winters sometimes freezes to the bottom. In April, 1897, the flow at Grand Forks reached 43,000 cubic feet per second. In October, 1932, it fell to thirteen cubic feet per second. "It approaches the former volume less frequently than the latter." Observe the im-

146

mense range between high and low water. At low water the river would hardly flush a two-hole privy, yet it was supposed to carry a dozen towns. One drop of culture B typhosis in a barrel of distilled water affects neither smell nor taste, but the man who drinks it may die.

Watch the law at work on the Connecticut River, beginning close to the Canadian line. Each town and city enumerated is labeled a "source of pollution" by the New England Planning Commission: Colebrook, North Stratford, Groveton, Lancaster, Woodville, Piermont, Lebanon, Charlestown, Hadley, Chicopee, Springfield, Enfield, Windsor Locks, Hartford, Glastonbury, Middletown, Haddam, Chester, Essex and Saybrook, where the accumulated disposal is dumped into Long Island Sound, to the despair of the shellfish. Four states are involved—New Hampshire, Vermont, Massachusetts and Connecticut. The basin covers 11,000 square miles and gives shelter to 1,230,000 people living in 355 townships. Twenty cities have more than 10,000 persons each. The townships operate 157 water systems, of which only twenty-two are purified. They operate 118 sewage systems of which 104 dump refuse into the rivers without any treatment whatever. Twenty-one of the latter are in urgent need of treatment, according to the commission. The Merrimac River is in a similar condition. I used to swim in this beautiful stream as a boy. Even then it was dangerous; now it is worth one's life to bathe below Manchester. There are 92 water systems in the Merrimac Valley of which only ten are purified; of 52 sewage systems only eleven are treated and there is urgent need for treatment in the case of thirteen cities.

Observe, however, the sad case of Peoria, Illinois. It was compelled by law to put in a sewage system, but a private industrial concern upstream is corrupting the river in a volume ten times greater than all the waste of Peoria.*

The Law of Dumping Down does not apply only to rivers. A hundred towns and many great cities pump sewage into the Great Lakes and pump drinking water out. Chicago's water supply is polluted by sewage from Indiana cities, Toledo's by Detroit, Niagara Falls' by Buffalo.

The Ohio basin is both a water supply and a sewage outlet. During low stages, "decreased and polluted supplies may cause outbursts of intestinal disturbances." Such disturbances may also come in high water. The *New York Times* carried a flood story in the spring of 1936, which reported 2,000 cases of gastroenteritis in the town of Coshocton, Ohio. The water supply had been flooded by the rising of the Tuscarawas River, and one-fifth of the town's population was seriously ill. This is one of those curious revolutions in the Great Wheel where a flood creates a shortage of water by poisoning the drinking supply. "Dr. W. B. Johnson of the City Health Department of Coshocton declared analysis of the city water showed presence of colon bacillus. Where there is colon bacillus, he said, there can also be typhoid."

Pollution grows worse as population moves from country to city. Says the National Resources Board: "Today many of the major cities discharge their untreated or partially treated sewage into adjacent bodies of water which have already exceeded their diluting capacity. In the future these

* Mississippi Valley Committee.

conditions are likely to become still more serious." There
are now approximately 7,100 public-water systems in the
country serving eighty million people with one billion cubic
feet a day. Twenty million of these people drink untreated
water; thirty million drink water treated with chlorine;
the balance use water treated with chlorine plus filtration.
Los Angeles holds the long-distance record with water
piped from Boulder Dam, 280 miles away; San Francisco's
supply comes from the Hetch Hetchy Reservoir, 170 miles
distant; New York taps the Catskill watershed, 150 miles
to the north; Boston brings water 75 miles from Lake
Wachusett. The average consumption for the country is
127 gallons per capita per day. Chicago is high with 270
gallons. Lowell, Massachusetts, is among the lowest with
50 gallons.

Sixty-eight million persons—half the population—discharge sewage through public systems. The sewage of
twenty-eight million persons receives some sort of treatment;
that from forty million persons "is discharged without
any treatment into inland streams, lakes or tidal waters."
The PWA has allocated money for 133 treatment projects
and for 420 straight sewer projects—which reflects the
fact that American cities want sewer pipes, but are not
much interested in where the contents go. Let them worry
about that downstream.

Pollution arises from domestic sewage, industrial wastes,
mine drainage and erosion. It has vicious effects on human
health, aquatic life, waterfowl, recreation, real estate values
and the hotel and resort business. The last two items
should impress Americans if the former do not. The twin

149

cities of St. Paul and Minneapolis alone report a $2,000,000 damage to property values. Indiana, Iowa and Virginia estimate losses running into the millions. Minnesota and Wisconsin, jointly, find a recreation loss of $1,500,000 due to pollution.

The most serious industrial wastes issue from textile mills, pulp mills, coal and gas works, leather works, sugar refineries, chemical industries, food canneries, creameries, packinghouses, oil fields, petroleum refining and rubber reclamation—a stench truly magnificent in combination! Some of this can be stopped at a net profit by making by-products from the waste—activated carbon from paper mills, for instance, or ferric sulphate from dye works. For the bulk of it, however, there is no solution except to spend the necessary funds to install treatment plants. The National Resources Board estimates that, for the country as a whole, 380 million dollars is necessary to bring pollution under reasonable control.

Mine drainage, among other things, costs the eastern railroads millions of dollars a year, by corroding and scaling locomotive boilers which take water from streams corrupted by coal mines. The WPA engages in more boondoggling by sealing abandoned coal mines in an attempt to prevent this loss. Up to 1935, 286 mines had been sealed, 13,000 drifts closed, 768,000 feet of crevice filled. Acidity in the Monongahela area has in consequence been reduced. For more than seven years the Allegheny River has been consistently acid, owing to mine drainage. This river is Pittsburgh's water supply.

At low water in the Willamette River in Oregon, no

dissolved oxygen at all is found. Salmon promptly die. Fishermen at the Golden Gate find their nets filled with raw sewage dumped by the city of Oakland into San Francisco Bay. The beaches of New Jersey and Long Island have frequently been made uninhabitable for bathers by New York City garbage. Here again I speak with considerable personal feeling, for I once had a cottage at Long Beach. In the lower East River off Manhattan, dissolved oxygen in summer is at zero—all cleansing power gone. Slips between the piers are collecting points for sewage sludge.

The Penobscot, Mohawk, Hudson, Delaware, Lehigh and Schuylkill rivers are grossly polluted and the Susquehanna is very bad. Many oyster beds in Chesapeake Bay have been condemned. The Fox, Milwaukee, Chicago, Calumet, and Maumee rivers are lined with industrial plants and are so contaminated that their usefulness for any other purpose is destroyed. In August, 1926, the upper Mississippi was so overloaded with impurities that dissolved oxygen was down to ten per cent for forty-five miles below Minneapolis. Conditions on the Missouri River are serious. Denver is active in befouling the South Platte River. Great Salt Lake is struggling to neutralize the loads of sewage which are heaped upon its waters. Waterfowl are seriously diseased from raw sewage dumped into the lagoons of the San Joaquin Valley. At low water on the Ohio, pools behind the navigation dams, filled with polluting sediment, become "obnoxious and dangerous" and swarm with bacteria.

Yet to control pollution in the Ohio, six states and the federal government must cooperate. No local unit, no state can do it alone. Because of the Law of Dumping Down, the whole basin is involved. State laws are totally inadequate; interstate compacts have not worked well in the past.

In the Ruhr district in Germany, the most heavily industrialized region in the world, all cities, towns, industries and mines in the basin have for years joined equitably in the cost of adequate waste-disposal works. All who contribute to the pollution are assessed, together with all who benefit by the control. The region bounded by the watershed line is the administrative area. Thus man and nature work together. In the United States, the various localities summon the courts to give them the right to dump their refuse on their neighbors' heads. There is no regional control and no adequate state control. Twelve states tender the problem of pollution to the part-time services of one sanitary engineer. Three states have no supervision whatsoever.

Pollution is one of the most vicious of the boomerangs. It hurts and befouls the continent, but, even more, it endangers the survival of man. It can be stopped if we are willing to plan for it on a basis of watershed areas and to pay for it.

Chapter X

DOWNSTREAM

THE pollution we found in the headwaters took us to the river mouth. Let us return to the upper courses and again begin our journey down. If we are following a western river, we come before long to a dam which diverts a part of the water through an irrigation ditch. The mother ditch may be large and deep. As it goes along it begins to divide and subdivide, until the smallest channels are foot-wide furrows, watering an individual field of rice, celery or grain.

Irrigation

West of the 100th meridian, agriculture either takes the gamble of dry farming the Great Plains or goes in for irrigation. Theoretically irrigation removes the gamble; practically the case is not so clear. The history of irrigation in America has been a long dismal record of speculation, excessive investment, excessive drain on the water supply, high maintenance charges and bankruptcy. The Central Valley is a case in point. There is nothing wrong about the principle of irrigation. It has worked and can work. Trouble comes when somebody tries to get rich quick. The lumber companies might have adopted the slogan "After me the deluge," the irrigation companies "After me the desert."

Irrigation is a very ancient practice. Egypt, Mesopotamia, India and China were and are extensively irrigated. Before the white man, the Indians of New Mexico diverted streams to a limited extent. J. Russell Smith estimates that one-third of the human race lives on irrigated land. China has more miles of channels than the United States has railroads. The rice terraces of the Igorots in Luzon are among the wonders of the world.

The first large-scale irrigators in America were the Mormons. Utah was the "deseret" claim chosen by Brigham Young. The snow-clad Wasatch Mountains, east of the Great Basin, caught the moisture from the Pacific winds. Many streams fell westward down their flanks and were turned into the dry lands near Great Salt Lake. Arid lands receive much sunlight and minerals lie rich in the topsoil. Water makes them very productive. The Mormons made a thriving garden out of their patch of Utah.

Properly safeguarded, irrigation does reduce the gamble of farming to a minimum. Rainfall no longer makes or breaks a crop. American projects have not been safeguarded. Irrigated lands have sold up to the fantastic figure of $4,000 an acre. Forests have been cleared from the mountains above, disturbing the flow of water at the right seasons, while excessive pumping has lowered artesian basins.

In 1930 about twenty-five million acres in the country were irrigated, roughly six per cent of all crop lands. The

National Resources Board estimates that another twenty-six
million acres is possible, seven million at a cost not to exceed
$100 per acre. No new projects, says the board, should be
undertaken at the present time. The potential acreage should
be held strictly in reserve.

Water is expensive. The labor of putting water on the
fields is expensive. From one to three feet of water is required
annually on each foot of ground. About one-third of all
irrigation acreage is controlled by private capital, one-third
by cooperative associations, one-sixth by local government
irrigation districts, one-tenth by the federal government
directly. Nearly every private enterprise has been in financial
difficulties at one time or another. Federal projects have
extended their amortization period from ten to twenty to
forty years. Irrigation, like its opposite, marsh-land drainage,
expands with a rush when prices are soaring, is extravagantly
overdone and before long leaves the settlers literally high
and dry. Acreage is often developed in excess of the water
supply. But the speculative promoters buy new Cadillacs.
No more piteous appeals reach the ears of distracted western
congressmen than those of ruined farmers on ruined irrigation projects.

The law makes matters worse. Under certain decisions in
California, riparian owners down the river can demand that
water come to them "unimpeded," which means that it
cannot be stored and conserved in the headwaters. This
creates a nuisance value of the first order, forcing investors
higher up to buy flooded lands lower down, not for what
they are worth as crop land, but for what they are worth
as a monopoly.

155

Supplementary Irrigation

Now let us swing back to rivers east of the 100th meridian. Here irrigation has been rare, except for special crops like rice. Recently, however, a different type known as *supplementary irrigation* has been receiving attention. I prophesy that the attention will become more and more pronounced. Supplementary irrigation is the use of water on the individual farm, over and above rainfall. The farmer builds little reservoirs to store the spring runoff, or he drives wells into the subsurface supply. Then he pumps this water upon his fields in the growing season by sprays, channels or porous hose connections. The latter is a pipe with holes in it which lies on the ground and allows water to leak out. There are more than 1,000 such installations in Michigan alone. If rainfall is inadequate at crucial periods, the supplementary water goes into action. Sometimes one sees it playing in the middle of a gentle rain. This looks foolish but happens to be remarkably good sense in that it adds enough to the gentle rain to make the total really count. I sometimes use this method on my tennis court.

Michigan potato yields have been raised from 100 to 435 bushels per acre by supplementary irrigation. Ohio apples, New Jersey potatoes, Virginia alfalfa and Georgia apples have shown remarkable increases. Farmers in the Rhone Valley in France rotate regularly between water and land farming—reservoir one year, grain next. Fish and waterfowl are "cropped" from the water, and the water increases soil fertility for the grain crop. The National Resources Board estimates that supplementary irrigation is feasible on 134 million acres in the United States—the equivalent of

2,500,000 farms in the humid areas—capable of delivering nine inches of water a year without damage to any natural balance.

Without damage? Indeed with great benefit to watershed control. The little reservoirs hold the spring runoff in the headwaters, the place where floods must ultimately be controlled. They attract wild fowl and fish. In addition they form reliable insurance against drought; they stabilize yields, increase production and quality, provide water for farm animals, bathrooms and fire protection. Cheap power is a most important consideration, for it mans the pumps. Average costs per acre with current at one cent per kilowatt-hour run about 23 cents to lay down an inch of water; at two cents, the cost jumps to 45 cents per acre; at three cents, to 68 cents per acre. Night pumping is better than day pumping, for evaporation is less. Thus the sprays work best at the time of the off-peak load. Here is an enormous outlet for electricity on the farm, tying in to conservation, flood control, more diversified crops and improved yields.*

Power

We have difficulty in getting down this river. Supplementary irrigation pulled us back to the headwaters. Let us try again. Below the dam for regular irrigation we find another powerful dam designed primarily for the generation of electricity. Sometimes, like Boulder Dam on the Colorado, it is a multiple-purpose structure for irrigation, city water supply (Los Angeles), flood control, recreation, fisheries and power. Sometimes, like Wilson Dam on the Tennessee, it is designed for navigation, flood control and power.

* For an excellent description of supplementary irrigation, see *Little Waters*.

"A higher percentage of pigpens in Norway are lighted by electricity than are American farmhomes."* About one out of eight farms in the United States is wired for electricity, including home plants, while the other seven are still on the kerosene, gasoline or candle standard. There is an enormous market for power in this country if it may be had cheaply enough. As energy is the basis of any civilization, it follows that increases in the energy supply tend to pay for themselves by performing useful work. In a pecuniary economy devoted to scarcity this logic is frequently perverted, but energy has a better chance than most commodities —particularly as it moves into the area of public business— to be produced for use rather than profit. I recently asked a noted electrical engineer what he regarded as the best policy in these circumstances. His answer was instantaneous: "Drench the country with power; uses will follow." It is something like Henry Ford putting millions of cheap cars on grossly inadequate highways. In a short time better highways appeared.

The great Bonneville Dam is rising on the Columbia River in Oregon. What is the state going to do with its new energy? The following list has been drawn up:

1. Increased per capita consumption on regular lines: more lighting, refrigeration, washing machines and similar uses.
2. Possible new industries.
3. Development of Oregon's natural resources with low-cost energy: converting lumber wastes into cellulose, Cellophane, pulp, etc.

* Cooperative League of America News Service, Feb. 26, 1936.

4. Discovery of new electrochemical and electrometallurgical processes.

5. Electrification of railroads.

6. Pumping water for irrigation (regular and supplementary).

7. Heating offices and homes with off-peak load.

8. Rural electrification.

In any sane world, more power means better living. I am not prepared to hold, in the mildly lunatic world which we enjoy, that such an outcome is inevitable. Some vested interest somewhere is always waiting to hit progress with a knotted club. More inanimate energy may result in more animate unemployment. The experience of Sweden shows that vested interests can be circumvented by a resolute citizenry and that more energy can mean better living. Sweden now has the highest standard of living in Europe. The Royal Board of Waterfalls owns the central transmission network, or grid, and certain important plants, producing more than one-third of all power in the nation. This yardstick keeps the private companies in line. Rates are low. The majority of farms are electrified. Cooperative societies contract for rural lines, paying an average of $35 per member as a capital charge to bring the line in. (In Washington and Idaho, by way of contrast, cooperatives pay $100 to $150 per member.) The government, through the royal board, inspects, prescribes accounts, audits, advises and helps manage the rural lines. Failures have been few. Rates run from one and three-quarters to two cents per kilowatt-hour. Urban rates run as low as one cent. The royal board earned 5.68 per cent on its investment in 1933 and 5.95 per cent in 1934.*

* Marquis W. Childs: *Sweden, The Middle Way.* Yale University Press, 1936.

ROSTER OF FEDERAL DAMS[1]

Dam	Purpose	Cost
1. Wilson, Ala.*	Navigation, power	$ 46,950,000
2. Norris, Tenn.*	Storage, power	36,000,000
3. Wheeler, Ala.†	Nav., flood, power	33,800,000
4. Pickwick L'ding, Tenn.†	Navigation, flood	26,700,000
5. Guntersville, Ala.‡	Navigation, flood	29,400,000
6. Chickamauga, Tenn.‡	Navigation, flood	31,600,000
7. Grand Coulee, Wash.†	Flood, irrigation, power	180,000,000
8. Boulder, Ariz.-Nev.*	Flood, irrigation, power	125,000,000
9. Friant, Calif.‡	Irrigation, power	15,000,000
10. Kennett, Calif.‡	Flood, irrigation, power	75,000,000
11. Keswick, Calif.‡	Flood, irrigation, power	7,000,000
12. Seminoe, Wyo.†	Flood, irrigation, power	8,500,000
13. Parker, Ariz.-Calif.†	Water supply, power	8,805,000
14. Roosevelt, Ariz.*	Irrigation, power	3,890,000
15. Fort Peck, Mont.†	Flood, irrigation, power	86,000,000
16. Conchas, N. M.†	Flood, water supply	9,000,000
17. Bonneville, Ore.-Wash.†	Navigation, power	31,000,000
18. Passamaquoddy, Me.†	Tidal power	37,732,000
19. Coolidge, Ariz.*	Flood, power	4,500,000
20. Tygart River, W. Va.†	Navigation, flood	15,000,000
21. Sardis, Miss.‡	Flood	9,000,000
22. Muskingum, Ohio†	Flood	23,000,000
23. Possum Kingdom, Tex.†	Flood, conversion	3,000,000
24. Shoshone, Wyo.*	Irrigation, power	1,500,000
25. Owyhee, Ore.*	Irrigation	5,400,000
26. Arrow Rock, Idaho*	Irrigation	4,300,000
27. Elephant Butte, N. M.*	Irrigation	4,100,000
28. Pathfinder, Idaho*	Irrigation	1,800,000
29. Horse Mesa, Ariz.*	Power	2,873,000
30. Mormon Flat, Ariz.*	Power	1,559,000
31. Stewart Mountain, Ariz.*	Power	2,515,000
32. Alcova, Wyo.†	Irrigation	3,339,000
33. Tieton, Wash.*	Irrigation	3,756,000
34. McKay, Ore.*	Irrigation	3,124,000
35. Bellefourche, S. D.*	Irrigation	1,230,000
36. Alamagorda, N. M.†	Irrigation	3,465,000
37. Taylor Park, Col.†	Irrigation	2,000,000

[1] *New York Times*, Feb. 23, 1936.
* Completed.
† Construction underway.
‡ Preliminary work started.

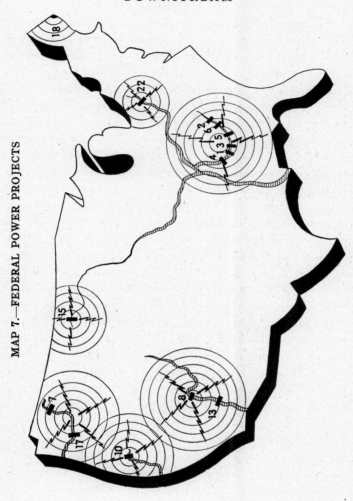

DOWNSTREAM

MAP 7.—FEDERAL POWER PROJECTS

The experience of our own Tennessee Valley Authority to date shows plainly that cheap power will be used and will create new markets for electric appliances. Power, however, is only one spoke in the Great Wheel. Floods are becoming so disastrous that they must be controlled. A major control device is a large reservoir to impound flood waters and equalize runoff. Large reservoirs demand large dams. When equalization waters are released, much natural energy is generated. Hydroelectric generators are not excessively expensive. Shall the surplus waters run to waste or shall they be used? If the dam is primarily for flood control, the capital cost of such power is next to nothing. Private power companies raise the complaint of unfair competition. Do the waters of this continent belong to them?

It looks as if we were going to get cheap power whether we use it or not. Congress, genuinely frightened by the floods of 1936, has authorized some 400 million dollars for control work, much of it reservoirs and dams. Water power cannot supply all our energy requirements, even if every rivulet were harnessed. Most of it has come and must continue to come from coal. Water power, however, possesses certain advantages. As a by-product of flood control, it is cheaper than coal. It lasts as long as the hydrologic cycle, while coal is a diminishing resource. In certain areas it is the more economical of the two if coal beds are far away.

Water power is a function of rainfall and topography. The Pacific northwest has heavy rains and many mountains, and thus great hydroelectric possibilities. The present national power plant, according to the National Resources Board, comprises:

162

	Kilowatts Installed
Water power	11,376,000
Fuel burners	42,921,000
Total	54,297,000

Water accounts for 50 per cent of all power in the Pacific states, Colorado and the South Atlantic states. The feasible undeveloped water power is 21,300,000 kilowatts, 14,000,000 in the Pacific and Colorado areas. The accompanying map locates thirty-seven federal dams and the table opposite gives their purposes and costs. The new flood-control appropriations will add more dams. There is danger, indeed, that we may go dam-crazy, neglecting the reservoirs which nature provides.

In the Taft administration engineers proposed a plan to use all the water of Niagara Falls to generate electricity. The American public rose on its hind legs and howled. So the water was split one-quarter for hydroelectric power and three-quarters for scenery. The falls thus furnished both mechanical energy and psychological energy, to quote Benton MacKaye. A great dam, such as Boulder or Norris, creates scenery of its own. I can testify to the psychological effect of the latter. It makes one feel stronger just to look at it.

If great dams are to function efficiently, they must be interconnected by transmission lines. The National Resources Board believes that the government should plan and control these lines, as is done in Sweden and England. It finds the present Mississippi system "a crazy patchwork of operating areas and a mass of individual unrelated generating units." Congested areas have a surplus, rural areas a

163

large deficit. The so-called British Grid has eliminated such confusion. By interconnecting generating units, both water and steam, under one control, reserve capacity and idle investment are greatly reduced and costs come down. The result is a balanced power load, continuity of service, greater efficiency. Power use is always 85 per cent or better. By way of contrast, the Keokuk-St. Louis-Detroit grid, operated by private companies, has an installed capacity of which only 66 per cent is used, measured by maximum peak load. Excess investment is 1,105,000 kilowatts. At $100 per kilowatt, chronically idle capital amounts to $110,500,000. "The present rate of growth of interconnection is too slow to meet the public need; the government should exercise its powers of leadership as it did during the War. . . . Great Britain has shown the way." Twelve unified grids are proposed by the National Resources Board for the United States in carefully delimited regions.

Private holding companies heretofore have had charge of networks, but their main interest has been in Wall Street. The result is a "crazy patchwork." If we are to benefit by the potential power of the new dams, keep energy costs low enough to encourage wide use and extend rural electrification as has been done in Scandinavia and England, the state must control the grids. It becomes the national wholesaler of energy, and, with this strategic position held, much generation of power, even much retailing, may remain in private hands. Cities and towns may take over retailing if they so elect. If the federal government controls the wholesale function, they may rest assured that no private company can milk them outrageously as in the past.

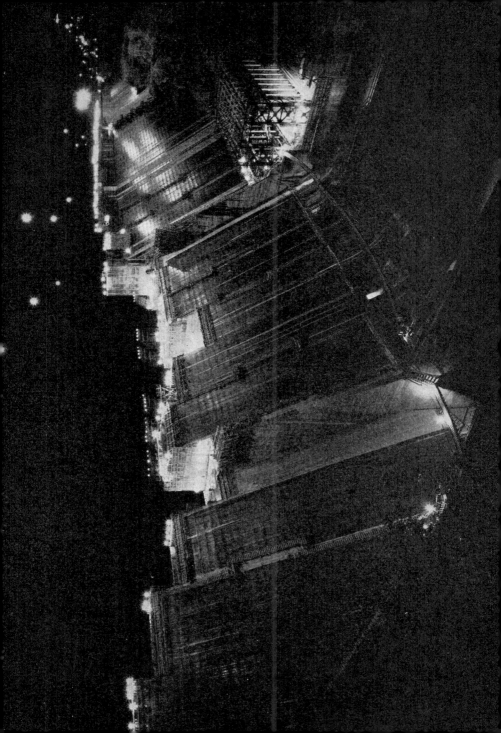

PLATE VII.—Norris Dam at night. (*Photo by Charles Krutch.*)

Rivers are for use. Every drop of water from mountaintop to ocean should be put to work. If dams are constructed, the waterpower should be converted into electricity wherever and whenever a reasonable prospect of consumption appears. Under my engineer's drenching theory, the word *reasonable* is subject to broad interpretation. Enlightened power interests will subscribe to this program. The others will continue to fight with all their billions, all their lobbies, all their doctored telegrams and all their power in the courts. They do not often bribe the judiciary; their means are more subtle. They *use* the courts, taking one appeal after another on the well-tested principle that "the power to delay is the power to destroy." But in the long run their fight is hopeless. Cheap energy is coming as surely as day follows night. The power gentlemen are in the position of the southern slave owners in 1850. They too were doomed, for the courses of history were against them. They too summoned the Supreme Court to their side in the Dred Scott decision. They too were rich, arrogant and unyielding. Will it take a bloody war to free the power slaves?

Navigation

As we float with the current from the tributaries into the main river, we find a string of barges laden with lumber, wheat, pig iron and cement. The steel tug which tows them is powered with a Diesel engine. Sailing craft dotted these rivers in 1787 and inland navigation was a cardinal matter. It was primarily to settle this question that the original Constitutional Convention was called in that year. Watersheds know no state boundaries, and something had to be done to adjudicate transport difficulties between states. Roads were bad and railroads nonexistent. In 1787 navigation was the most important of river functions. The Supreme Court, passing on the validity of the TVA in 1936, held to this concept. Yet in the real world of 1936, navigation has fallen from first place in the hierarchy of river uses to near the bottom. It is still important in limited sections, but railroads, trucks, pipe lines, transmission lines and air lines have cut away a large part of its utility. Power, flood control, water supply and irrigation have scrambled ahead of it. Recreation is probably equally important in 1936, and will grow in importance every year.

As routes for transport, rivers have many disadvantages. They are crooked rather than direct. They do not always follow traffic movements. They require costly transshipment of goods in many cases. The variation in water level at different seasons makes docking and warehousing difficult. In the north, rivers are closed by ice for months at a time. An excessively canalized channel changes a free-flowing river into a series of slack-water pools, which encourage pollution.

The National Resources Board is unenthusiastic about the 850-mile channel in the Missouri River. Large sums have been spent with little prospect of actual transport use. The Ohio, the main channel of the Mississippi and the Tennessee have more utility, especially for heavy goods like sand, gravel, rock, asphalt and coal. Navigation may well play its part when flood control, power, irrigation and other uses are also involved.

To the close of 1932, the federal government had spent about two billion dollars on river and harbor improvement.

This was the famous "pork barrel," on the whole well named. Outlays for navigation, as for irrigation, have undoubtedly been overdone. They should be promoted only after rigorous impartial surveys. A sound river policy would include navigation when the flow of traffic in bulk commodities from point A to point B on the river warranted it, and such a policy should be as hard-boiled toward the railroads—which are always seeking to divert traffic from waterways—as toward the factor of actual use. If navigation costs are shared with power, flood control and other purposes, and if point B on the stream requires a large volume of bulk goods from point A, water transport may well be the cheapest form of all. The National Resources Board reports a study of comparative transport costs in man-hours, including operation and maintenance:

MAN-HOUR COSTS OF MOVING 1,000 TONS ONE MILE

	Man-hours
Man with a pack	20,000
Man with a wheelbarrow	10,000
Five-ton trucks on cement road	50
All Class I railroads	6
Inland Waterways Corporation (Mississippi River)	5
Pipe lines reporting to Interstate Commerce Commission	2

This table is an impressive exhibit of the power age. It shows that fluids pumped through a pipe are transported at one-ten-thousandth the expense, in terms of human effort, with which they can be carried on a man's back. It shows that waterways tend to shade railroads on a straight haul. It does not show, however, all the variables of any given shipment, which must be the final arbiter. If a man in St. Louis has lumber to ship to a man in New Orleans,

167

and if the man in New Orleans is in no hurry and wants the lumber for use near the dock, the waterway is his best medium. But if he wants to transship the lumber to Tupelo, Mississippi, or if he wants fresh vegetables rather than lumber, then either the railroad or the truck or a combination of both may better serve his need.

High Water and Low

Well down the main river, past the dams, the irrigation channels and the barges, we come to the levees and the most dramatic, if not the most serious, of all the basin's problems. A given quantity of water comes down the river each year. Under primeval conditions, natural reservoirs leveled this runoff through the months. The flood peak, we will say, was 70, and the low-water level 30. Now man destroys or weakens the reservoirs. Approximately the same amount of water comes down. But the flood peak rises to 90 and the low water drops to 10. A peak of 70 is a brisk spring freshet, a peak of 90 a disastrous flood. A low of 30 marks an uncomfortable dry spell, a low of 10 a serious drought.

H. H. Bennett of the Soil Conservation Service reports the floods of 1936 the worst on record in many areas. Why? Because natural reservoirs have been progressively weakened. There is less porosity in the soil, fewer roots, steeper tilled slopes. Worse still is silting, which makes rivers increasingly unmanageable, "subject to more and more violent interruptions and alterations of stream flow." Real flood control, says Mr. Bennett, must begin in the soil itself.

In 1936 the Merrimac, Connecticut, Hudson, Delaware, Susquehanna, Potomac, Allegheny and Ohio all went wild.

PLATE VIII.—FLOOD. (Photo by Charles Krutch.)

The Potomac was up twenty-six feet at Washington and long barriers of sandbags protected government buildings. Chain Bridge, carrying water pipes to a large population in Virginia, was closed to traffic and threatened to go out. Pittsburgh was under ten to twenty feet of water and was without lights, transport or power. The life of 700,000 people was paralyzed. The food supply was ruined, the steel industry at a standstill. In Steubenville, Ohio, the water supply was contaminated by flood waters and medical authorities rushed antityphoid serum from Columbus. At Bellaire, the hospital sent out a distress call for water as the city's supply failed.

But in the Winooski Valley in Vermont all was well. A bad flood in 1927 had drowned 55 people in this region. In 1936 just as much water came down, but not a life was lost, not a highway or railway washed out, not a farmhouse damaged. Three flood-control dams built by the federal government held the water and saved the valley. They were finished with the aid of CCC workers just in time.

Artificial flood control, other than work in the headwaters, takes three major forms:

1. Storage reservoirs, as in the Winooski Valley.
2. Channel improvements to increase capacity of flow.
3. Levees and dikes to wall the water in.

The last has been the chief device for 200 years, and every year it grows more preposterous. The alluvial valley of the Mississippi was subject to floods even under primeval conditions. But it was covered with heavy timber. The water spread into natural side basins and wandered to the Gulf

169

by various routes so that no great damage was done. In 1717 the first levee was constructed at New Orleans. For the next hundred years levees spread slowly up the valley to the Arkansas River. It was the duty of abutting landholders to build them. The Swamp Land Acts of 1850 encouraged states to construct levees, and earthen mounds became continuous from New Orleans to the upper limits of the alluvial valley. Old Man River was walled in. Was he?

In 1879 Congress came into the picture and appointed the Mississippi River Commission to establish a grade line for levees from Cairo to the Gulf. But the line was not high enough. The river broke through. In 1898 the grade was raised five feet. The flood of 1912 overwhelmed it. In 1914 it was raised again with a three-foot margin of safety beyond. The total cost was now prodigious. The flood of 1927 tumbled over the margin of safety and swamped the whole valley —the worst rampage on record. Another five to ten feet was called for, plus floodways running parallel to the river, guarded by "fuse-plug" levees. The cost was 300 million dollars—about thirty-five million dollars per grade foot. In all there are now 1,825 miles of levees averaging twenty-one feet in height. The higher they go the more they cost, while the *river bottom itself tends to rise, owing to silt from eroded fields.* Soon the river will be flowing on a mound between higher mounds, well above the surrounding country. Give her another ten feet, boys, at 50 million dollars a foot! There is no end to this mad race except complete victory for the river. Some day it may sweep the valley clean— levees, towns, cities, fields, farms, railroads, highways, industries—in the wildest, most disastrous flood in history.

Big floods are unpredictable, since they depend on a conjunction of circumstances—especially heavy snowfall, violent rains in March, frozen earth to speed the runoff. People forget these things, as peasants around Vesuvius forget eruptions. But they always come! God help the people of the Mississippi Valley when the next one comes! The critical point in the whole system is Cairo. Here the Ohio comes in. Just east of it the Tennessee joins the Ohio, and just east of that the Cumberland enters. What the TVA is doing at Norris may some day help to save New Orleans. But we are speaking of levees only, and what the TVA is doing is another and happier story.

Man is a greedy animal. If he had built his levees a little back from the banks, leaving the natural flood basin in forest and bird colonies, he would have had a better chance of controlling the river. But no. Crop lands have crowded in on the natural flood plain, behind levees built close to the banks. A large part of the increasing flood damage in recent years is due to the occupation of river banks and valleys by cities, towns, industrial plants, bridges, railroads and highways, as well as by farms. We are hemming our rivers in below, and thus far have taken few steps to control them from above.

The great Mississippi flood of 1927 inundated 18,000 square miles, killed 246 people, drove 750,000 from their homes and did 300 million dollars of damage to property. Silt is rising on the floor of the Rio Grande precisely as in the Mississippi. But without levees the rising river waterlogs the surrounding country. On the Missouri River, 2,275,000 acres of land, twenty-six cities and 730,000 people are subject to floods. Losses on the Red River in Arkansas mount to ten million dollars in a season. Controls on the Arkansas River are grossly inadequate and losses reach fifteen million.

The engineering policy of flood control for 200 years has been to get the water off the land by drain, channel, levee or culvert. In big streams, dredge the channel and hustle it faster. The policy is vicious, stupid and wrong. The only intelligent program is to *hold* the water in the soil or in the artesian basin, pond, lake and farm reservoir. When this is not enough, or cannot readily be done, hold it with big dams and artificial reservoirs.

Beavers were butchered to make ugly hats. In Oregon, surviving members of the clan are being transplanted to the headwaters of streams, there to build dams and help hold the floods. Levees seek to control high water at the wrong end. Beavers have the right idea.

Taking out the peaks and valleys of stream flow does not eliminate drought insofar as drought is caused by inadequate rainfall. It does however mitigate its effects. Just as lowering a flood crest by twenty per cent usually precludes all serious damage, so raising the low-water stage helps greatly in a drought. Adequate water supply is maintained, pollution is checked, cattle can drink, irrigation ditches carry life-giving fluid, generator wheels turn, barges deliver their freight.

In the great drought of 1934, irrigation areas were obliged to concentrate on watering livestock with nothing to spare for crops. By August all storage facilities in Utah with one exception were exhausted. In parts of the Great Plains and the Great Basin and in the Imperial Valley of California,

172

not only were crops and pastures destroyed, but there was an acute shortage of domestic water. Had Boulder Dam been operating in 1934, it could have saved the Imperial Valley. Seven million head of cattle and five million sheep, gaunt with thirst, were purchased by the FERA. Relief grants totaled 78 million dollars. The total direct damage to agriculture was estimated by the National Resources Board at five billion dollars. "All this leads to the conclusion that water conservation for drought insurance is feasible for much of the arid regions, but that to be effective it must be predicated upon basic hydrologic facts and carried out according to a planned program of water and land use." Drought control is the other side of flood control, and both are implicit in the planned development of a watershed area.

As I write in July, 1936, a drought which already has caused a billion dollars worth of crop damage is searing the prairies, the Great Plains and parts of the south. The area most seriously stricken is on the 100th meridian zone in the Dakotas. Here we remember the transfer from natural grass to wheat speeded up transpiration, reduced infiltration and seriously depleted ground water storage. Without storage, a normal dry cycle quickly develops into a disaster. Thousands of families, their wheat burned to brown stubble a few inches high, their cattle bellowing with thirst, their very homes made uninhabitable by dust and sand, have commenced a great migration. Whither? No one unless it be the Resettlement Administration has the remotest idea.

There is no reason to suppose that the climate in the west is changing. There is every reason to suppose that for thousands of years cycles have moved from wet to dry and back again, that it has often been just as hot as in 1934 or 1936. But never before has so much of the original grassland been in crops and never have natural reservoirs been so depleted. Where the buffalo may have endured a thoroughly uncomfortable season, man encounters a fiery hell.

Floods encourage silt, and silt by raising stream bottoms encourages floods. Of all the power dams which have been studied from North Carolina to Mississippi, there is not one that is not already silted to the level or above the level of the penstocks. Freeboards have been installed in an attempt to increase the head. These dams, as a class, are doomed to uselessness, according to H. H. Bennett, not in fifty or seventy-five years, but in the immediate future. Reservoir studies of 56 dams made by the Soil Conservation Service in 1934 showed thirteen major dams averaging thirty feet in height completely filled by silt during an average life of twenty-nine years. The Austin Dam in Texas was choked in five years and completely filled in fifteen. The Harding Reservoir in California was gagged in *one month* by heavy rains following a forest fire in the water-shed. It is folly to build reservoirs without erosion control above. Remember Ducktown.

Our journey down the basin ends at the river mouth, but problems still pursue us. There are three problems, to be specific: pollution poisons harbor waters; low river stages allow too much salinity in harbors, destroying shellfish; salt water backs up the river and ruins valuable crop lands, as in the delta of the Central Valley.

The Great Wheel turns. From the raindrop on the height of land, down a thousand miles to the salt water of the

174

ocean, one problem locks with another, and there is no solution, either for the continent or for man, except in coordinated control that comprehends all problems. None can be settled by itself alone. Of this fact the outstanding illustration is perhaps the mad building of levees—or is it the construction of mighty dams with no provisions to prevent them from choking to death?

A drainage basin, big or little, is a region through which water moves. No act of man can permanently halt this flow of power, nor even diminish it to an appreciable degree. The water must come down—we could not stop it if we would. We can, however, figuratively as well as literally, canalize it so that it will do what we want it to do and not do what we do not want it to do.*

Boulder Dam

Here is Boulder Dam, the most stupendous structure ever built. The drainage basin of the Colorado River covers 240,000 square miles. The main river is 1,300 miles long and flows through six states and two nations. Rainfall varies from ten inches along the Green River to sixty inches on the continental divide. The central basin is a great plateau, 5,000 to 8,000 feet above the sea, cut through by the Grand Canyon, 400 miles long and sometimes a mile deep. Against the rock walls of this canyon, Boulder Dam braces its massive shoulders. The basin has a sparse population but is the center of many important economic activities. Copper, lead, zinc, gold and silver are mined in its mountains, oil within its borders. Large irrigation projects tap its waters, including one for the Imperial Valley. Grasslands try to support

* Mississippi Valley Committee.

175

grazing. Tourists and health seekers have provided the basis for a considerable industry. The Colorado River, says the National Resources Board, is the determining factor in the development of the American southwest.

Boulder Dam was built for four purposes: flood control, the stabilization of irrigation, electric power and water supply for Los Angeles and other cities. A fifth has been added automatically—recreation on the great lake which backs 115 miles upstream. The lake is being stocked with bass and other fish. Licenses for resort hotels, tourist camps, dude ranches and boat lines have been applied for through the Bureau of Reclamation which—thank God!—controls the shores. The dam was delivered to the government on Sunday, March 1, 1936, two years ahead of schedule. It stands 727 feet above bed rock, is 1,282 feet wide and tapers from a thickness of 635 feet at the bottom to 45 feet at the top, over which runs a highway. In 1935 a devastating *flood* in the lower valley was forestalled by the dam. It filled part of its vast reservoir with flood waters, and then released them in the summer and fall, preventing a devastating *drought*. Double action. The drought of 1934 cost the Imperial Valley ten million dollars. This would have paid for a lot of cement.

The total cost of the dam and the collateral dams and engineering works which integrate with it will be close to half a billion dollars. It is expected that the whole cost will be amortized through power sales over the next fifty years. The government will operate and maintain the dam, reservoir, pressure tunnels, outlet works, penstocks and shutoff valves. The city of Los Angeles and the Southern

California Edison Company will operate jointly the generators and transmission lines.

The engineering work has been better than the political work. Seven states, the federal government and Mexico are all involved, and the rows have been stupendous. Arizona still refuses to ratify the compact. It looked for a time as if the dam would never be built. There has been precious little watershed thinking on the part of the contestants. What can I get out of it? has been the dominant motive. The Supreme Court stands on the bank, anxiously admonishing the Colorado River not to violate the Constitution.

What a blessing it would have been if watersheds, whose boundaries always follow the height of land, had been taken by our ancestors as political boundaries too. A river is the worst possible boundary because its problems lie equally on both banks. So New Jersey and New York, abutting on the Hudson, maul each other in the courts from generation to generation.

Chapter XI

CREATURES OF LAND AND WATER

IT IS as easy to become sentimental about wild animals as about primeval trees. When emotion rather than knowledge is guide, it may lead to a situation where the S. P. C. A. needs to be called in. "The demand," says the Mississippi Valley Committee, "for complete conservation or prohibition of all killing has led in certain instances to overstocking of areas with game and extensive starvation and disease because of lack of food." Thus deer on the Kaibab plateau in Arizona were overprotected and they multiplied beyond their natural food supply. The balance of nature can be upset by overconservation as well as by underconservation.

The continent provides a home for man and other creatures. If the creatures were exterminated, the position of man would become untenable. Insects, with such natural enemies as birds eliminated, would make short work of him. Certain creatures have to go when man comes in. Buffalo and cattle cannot jointly crop the Great Plains. Grizzly bears and mountain lions make poor neighbors

around ranch and farm. Foxes and hens do not cooperate. As
in the case of forest, grass and water, the problem is to find
the facts, consult the ecologists and determine a practicable
working arrangement with our fellow tenants. Not only is
there room for both of us, but we are the debtors when all
is said and done. Wild animals got along nicely without
white men for a hundred thousand years on North America,
but the palefaces cannot get along without wild animals.
We not only need them as the first line of defense against the
insect menace, but we need their furs, hides and oils—such
as cod-liver oil—in certain manufactures, we need them for
an important form of recreation in hunting and fishing, and
we need their life and beauty about us whenever we leave
the city. What would a home in the country be without
birds and beasts within sight and earshot? One might as
well live in Sahara.

The Insect Menace

In six months a diligent pair of house flies can have six
trillion offspring, equipped to carry at least thirty diseases.
Pests eat $250,000,000 of textile crops a year and a good
part of the apple crop. In Washington and Oregon pine
beetles destroy eight times as much timber as fires—though
it must be admitted that fire weakens those trees it does not
kill and thus provides easier access for pests. "They want,"
writes C. C. Furnas, "our clothes, houses, potatoes, apples,
corn, wheat, cotton, shade trees and even our very blood.
They take them." More than 500,000 varieties of insects
have been collected and named. Their adaptation is marvelous. Cockroaches thrived in the coal age; their digestive

systems can assimilate mustard plasters, Egyptian mummies and Jefferson's *Manual on the Constitution*. If men had legs relatively as strong as some insects, they could reach the moon in a few hops. One pair of plant lice can theoretically produce in a season enough progeny to outweigh the human population of the earth fivefold. Larval midges can live in water at 120° Fahrenheit.*

Before the coming of white men, the balance of nature kept insects and pests under reasonable control. We have weakened nature's resistance. Recent studies in natural grasslands show that the number of pests does not become significantly large until overgrazing sets in. In the Wichita National Forest runs a fence carrying two strands of barbed wire. On one side of the fence grasshoppers are a blight and on the other they do no damage. Cannot a grasshopper climb a fence? He can. The strange division is due to cattle. Overgrazing occurs on one side of the fence and not on the other. Take the elm-tree borer: he thrives only in exposed and sunlit places. Under natural conditions elms grow in shady locations and escape the borer. We plant elms, or leave them unprotected, in the middle of fields and meadows.

Birds are the greatest of pest destroyers, although bats, shrews, moles, squirrels, armadillos, badgers and the lowly skunk do very well. In 1907 there was a plague of field mice in the Humboldt River region of Nevada. The news was broadcast along the flyways and gulls, hawks and owls flocked to the scene. In a month they devoured nearly a million mice. Forty-five species of birds descended upon the alfalfa weevil at Great Salt Lake. A house wren brings an insect to its young on the average of every two minutes all

* Bernard Jaffe: *Outposts of Science*. Simon & Schuster, Inc., 1935.

180

day long. Twenty-five species of birds feed on the clover weevil, 25 on the potato beetle, 36 on the codling moth, 46 on the gypsy moth, 49 on house flies, 67 on bill bugs, 98 on cutworms, 120 on leaf hoppers, 168 on wire worms. There may be as many as three billion breeding birds in the United States, most of them insectivorous. There are—or were—an equal number of migrants, stopping about two months on their flights from Mexico to Canada. Where should we be without this protecting army?

Hunters

Two varieties of hunters may be identified: butchers and sportsmen. The former are either businessmen intent on a quick profit like the lumber barons, or sadists who have something wrong with their glands. Pot hunters, they have sometimes been called. If the wild-creature population were turned over exclusively to their mercies, there would not be a living thing left in a decade. With dynamite, net and machine gun they would wipe bare the lands and waters of the continent and insects would complete the destruction. One of this precious crew boasted that in a single year he had killed 139,000 game birds and animals. A single hunter in the last century butchered 7,000 canvasback ducks in one season. Chesapeake Bay hunters armed with swivel guns killed 1,500 ducks in eight hours for the New York market.

Pot hunters have exterminated the passenger pigeon and the heath hen. Of the trumpeter swan, perhaps 50 wild birds still survive. Helped by pollution and the damming of rivers, pot hunters are well on their way to exterminating the Pacific halibut, the Pacific salmon, the Puget Sound

181

salmon, the Atlantic salmon, the sturgeon and the shad. They are rapidly reducing the numbers of bluefin, blackfin and bloater in the Great Lakes. On every coast their assaults on the lobster, oyster, shrimp, scallop and clam steadily reduce the population. The national oyster catch declined more than a third from 1901 to 1926.

Let all the American people be warned that to the really greedy and savage pot hunter, no bird is sacred, and no bird is safe. But for protecting laws mercilessly enforced, the pot hunters would kill all our songbirds, woodpeckers, tree protectors, shore birds, herons and cranes, in about three years.*

NORTH AMERICAN BIRD†
Extinct

Passenger pigeon

Great auk

Labrador duck

Heath hen

Guadalupe caracara

Guadalupe towhee

Guadalupe rock wren

Threatened

Eskimo curlew

Carolina parakeet

Sharp-tailed grouse

Swallow-tailed kite

Butterball duck

Upland plover

Golden plover

Buff-breasted sandpiper

Woodcock

Whooping crane

Great white heron

Atwater prairie chicken

Masked bobwhite

California vulture

Red-bellied hawk

Everglade kite

Cape Sable sparrow

Bachman warbler

Dusky kinglet

Flamingo

Roseate spoonbill

Trumpeter swan

Harlequin duck

Redhead duck

Ringneck duck

Lesser scaup

* William T. Hornaday.

† Based on report of hearings on agricultural appropriations for 1937.

CREATURES OF LAND AND WATER

NORTH AMERICAN MAMMALS

Extinct

Maine giant mink
California grizzly bear
Tejon grizzly bear
Texas grizzly bear
Plains grizzly bear

Gull Island meadow mouse
Pacific white-tailed deer
Merriam elk
Badlands mountain sheep
Texas mountain sheep

Threatened

White Mountain dwarf shrew
Spotted bat
Glacier bear
Arizona grizzly bear
Black-footed ferret
Wolverine
Sea otter
Kit fox
Plains wolf
Guadelupe fur seal
Gray whale
Atlantic right whale
Greenland right whale

Monk seal
Hooded seal
Pacific walrus
Atlantic walrus
Eastern fox squirrel
Peninsula fox squirrel
San Joaquin kangaroo rat
Beach meadow mouse
Key deer
Button willow elk
Nelson mountain sheep
Sierra mountain sheep
Florida manitee

The sportsman, as contrasted with the pot hunter, has no business interest in killing and no sadistic perversion to satisfy. He believes in giving animals a chance, a fair gamble with death. He flicks a trout stream with a fly rather than mining it with a worm. He does not go duck hunting with a gatling gun. Above all, he wants to see the game population grow and he is a belligerent conservationist. I cannot admire his sport, for I kill only when no other food is to be had, but I respect his attitude. Sportsmen have taken the lead in protective legislation. I suspect that, if the animals and birds threatened with extinction in the above lists by some miracle survive, it will be chiefly the sportsmen who save them.

Observe the strange case of the Atlantic shad. The catch in 1900 was 50 million pounds. Now it is down to ten or twelve million. Many fishing villages have been stranded as a result. The Federal Bureau of Fisheries transplants young shad to the Pacific where they are well protected by the California Fish Commission. In 1925 two million pounds were iced and shipped clear across the continent and "solemnly sold as the great and rare delicacy of the Atlantic waters." The sequence, according to Van Hise, is this:

We destroy an abundant food supply by ruthless exploitation. And thus change a necessity into a luxury.

At considerable expense we set up the industry on the Pacific coast and show it can be made to flourish if reasonable protection is afforded the shad.

We then ship the fish back 3,000 miles to the original home waters, to cater to the luxury trade.

The Plymouth colony in 1620 took out its charter "to serve God and to fish." God, we trust, has been served, but the fish have not. This great, rich resource is as desolated as the grasslands.

The island of Nantucket lies on the edge of the Gulf Stream, well off the coast of Massachusetts. It was once the greatest whaling center in the world and supported a prosperous population. The whales were killed off, and the island, deprived of its major resource, sought to sustain itself with fish of smaller dimensions. The great August run of bluefish, the abundant shellfish, mackerel and cod all gave opportunity for hardy men in little boats to make a living. But the hardy men, like their brothers on the main-

184

land, subscribed to the concept of infinity. There was no end to land and no end to fish. Land did end at the Golden Gate. The fish supply of Nantucket began to decline. If the recreation industry had not invaded the island in the form of summer visitors, yachtsmen and sunbathers, it is probable that in due time the sole inhabitants would have been the keepers of lighthouses. The fishing business was almost bankrupt.

A large landowner on the island, Bassett Jones, became interested in the conservation of marine life. He helped the fishermen to organize a cooperative association whose purpose, instead of a scramble to kill and sell before the other man, was to increase the basic supply so that all might share in a larger catch. There was no uplift in the organization but a very practical program. The hardy men, individualists since time out of mind, got the point. They set out seeding beds, they protected the oncoming generations, they entered into cooperative arrangement about the catch. You see their white buoys all about Nantucket waters. When I visited Mr. Jones in the summer of 1935, the scallops were coming back, the lobsters were coming back; Nantucket was reestablishing its resource base. Here, in a miniature world, the whole continental tragedy had been enacted and the way to its solution made plain. The fishermen have turned from defying nature to working with her, and they are beginning to reap their reward.

The Flyways

Let us examine the effects of land use on birds, especially migratory birds. Four great flyways have been identified by ornithologists, banding the country from Mexico to Canada. They have been named Atlantic, Mississippi, Central and Pacific. For these flyways birds have a deep ancestral instinct and they die rather than desert them. It is like the salmon returning to his own breeding stream after voyaging all over the Pacific. "Heavy overshooting, drainage of marsh lands, agricultural activities, and drought have reduced the numbers of migratory waterfowl over the entire continent, but the decrease has been more rapid in the Central and Pacific areas."* If a species is exterminated on any one of the flyways, the region will remain barren. Birds of the same species on other flyways will not desert their ancestral run.

North they come over the flyways to the nesting grounds —wild geese, ducks, swans, cranes, rails, curlews, plovers, wild pigeons, nighthawks, whippoorwills, meadow larks, kinglets, tanagers, waxwings, robins, thrushes, bitterns, gannets, herons, shearwaters, terns. By banding their legs with aluminum markers, scientists and bird lovers are beginning to learn how they come and what routes they follow. Why they come and what compasses they use to guide their long journeys remain unknown. At altitudes from 2,000 to 3,000 feet, they cross the streams, lakes, woodlands, mountains and cities of the continent. "Like formations of the old Roman phalanx, they wing their way to the honk of the geese, and the quack of the leading duck, with answering calls along the line. They pass through in utter darkness, following their leader; and so they go—a mystery that our

* F. C. Lincoln: *The Waterfowl Flyways of North America*. U. S. Department of Agriculture, 1935.

186

scientists have not solved."* Ducks travel from 44 to 59 miles an hour; geese from 42 to 55 miles an hour; smaller perching birds from 20 to 37 miles an hour. The arctic tern is the greatest traveler of them all. His flyway is from pole to pole—from arctic to antarctic and back again.

The nesting grounds of the waterfowl migrants are largely in Canada, but a great wedge extends down into the United States. It stretches from the Canadian line to the Ruthhaven marshes in Iowa, to the Nebraska sand hills, to the Black Hills of the Dakotas, and northwest to Lake Bowdoin in Montana. The breeding ground once furnished ideal conditions for water-fowl—prairie grasses, a thousand lakes and streams, a million snow-filled potholes, few enemies, perfect isolation. The ceaseless movements of the waterfowl were the essence of the prairie country. Century after century they returned to the broad plains to rear their young. What a sight it must have been when birds and buffalo were on the prairies together! Buffalo moved as few other quadrupeds have ever moved, in great multitudes, like armies in review, covering many square miles at once. There was a thunder of hoofs on the plain, and countless wings above them.

The wings are sadly depleted now. The prairie, as we have seen, has been broken up. The war demand turned many a large pothole and slough from producing ducks to producing wheat. The unbroken sod of upland bench and swale in the *coteau du Missouri* was first plowed in the war years, its priceless store of moisture to be sucked up by the

* Harry B. Hawes: *Fish and Game—Now or Never*. D. Appleton-Century Co., 1935.

187

parched prairie wind. The water in the potholes and many lakes failed before the young ducks were able to leave the ground. They never left it.

Large lake basins that formerly served to regulate the fluctuations of the water table were drained to answer the cry for more grain, and marshes became heavily capitalized drainage districts. In many instances these ventures were unsuccessful, yet the natural ecological conditions were so changed that migratory waterfowl could not resume their nesting there. Power developments made inroads. Road building in the last decade resulted in many a fine chain of canvasback and redhead nesting potholes being cut by grades and inevitably drained.*

When grain prices soared, farmers eliminated hedgerows and thickets and replaced them with barbed wire, thus securing a few extra feet of crop land. The result was more wind erosion and fewer birds.

The last normal nesting season was in 1929. Depression came for birds as well as for man. The subsequent five years of drought struck the final blows. "This nesting ground now lies a desert so far as its former millions of waterfowl are concerned." Seventy-five per cent of the original breeding lands are now under the plow or totally dried up. The true sportsman realizes that there remains less than half the reserves which should be sent back north each spring, that three species of ducks—the redhead, the ringneck, and the lesser scaup—are all but extinct and that other species are critically reduced. He knows that the agencies of destruction are strong and organized.

* J. Clark Salyer: A Program for Waterfowl Restoration. U. S. Department of Agriculture, 1934.

188

PLATE IX.—Winter sports in northern Louisiana: shooting wild pigeons. (*Sketched by Smith Bennett: "The Illustrated Sporting and Dramatic News," July 3, 1875. Reprinted by permission from "The Passenger Pigeon in Ontario" by Margaret H. Mitchell, University of Toronto Press.*)

(Facing page 189)

In 1857, when the slaughter of passenger pigeons was becoming ominous, the legislature of Ohio considered a bill for their protection. A committee heard the testimony pro and con and reported as follows:

The passenger pigeon needs no protection. Wonderfully prolific, having the vast forests of the north as its breeding ground, traveling hundreds of miles in search of food, it is here today and elsewhere tomorrow, and no ordinary destruction can lessen them, or be missed from the myriads that are yearly produced.

The prophecy was no better than the grammar. "Else-where" meant in eternity; the last pigeon died in 1914.

In 1910 the first laws were passed against excessive hunt-ing for the market. The bird population promptly rose and continued to rise for about ten years. Then the increase in the sadistic breed of pot hunters, duly equipped with licenses and high-powered shotguns, turned the index down. It has been going down ever since. At last accounts there were 5,738,000 licensed hunters in the country. Probably not one in five has learned to be a sportsman.

Game animals, on the whole, have fared better than birds. They are larger and harder for bootleggers to hide. More game preserves have been provided for them, like Yellow-stone Park for the grizzlies. Deer, moose and black bear are actually increasing. Caribou, antelope, mountain sheep and elk are on the ragged edge. When the plow came to the Great Plains, elk lost their winter range. They were forced to remain in the high mountains, "where they suffered

189

pitifully, many dying from starvation or disease in hard winters."

Mountain lions, wolves, coyotes and bobcats are competent game destroyers, but the greatest predatory animal is man. The National Resources Board estimates that, to protect our upland game animals, twenty-one million acres of refuges are needed in the arid lands and mountains of the west; to protect waterfowl, seventeen million acres of protected breeding grounds. A chain of resting stations should be established up and down the four great flyways, of from 10,000 to 50,000 acres each and about 300 miles apart. The federal government has launched a bold program. The government of Canada is cooperating in respect to migratory game. So are many states and every genuine sportsman.

The life and vigor of the continent was reflected in its forests, grasses, beasts, birds and fishes. These in turn took their nourishment from a healthy, growing soil and clear abundant waters. All were components of the Great Wheel, dependent upon it, helping it turn. All belong in any plan which man may make for maintaining the vitality of the continent. Watch a child in the country. Nothing excites his interest like living creatures. With hundreds of generations back of him, he knows instinctively that his world is their world too.

> I saw with open eyes
> Singing birds sweet
> Sold in the shops
> For the people to eat,
> Sold in the shops of
> Stupidity Street.

I saw in vision
The worm in the wheat
And in the shops nothing
For people to eat,
Nothing to eat in
Stupidity Street.

—Ralph Hodgson.

Chapter XII

BELOW THE SURFACE

SO FAR the subjects of our study have been living animals and plants, and waters and winds that move with a kind of life bequeathed them from the sun—a total organism which, if maintained in equilibrium, goes on to perpetuity. Now we plunge below the earth cover to find dead rock, dead metal and the carbonized bones of plants and animals dead these million years.

Minerals are being raised from the earth in vast quantities. For every ton that comes up from its geological bed, a ton less remains below. Unlike the living, moving things, mineral resources diminish year by year no matter how carefully they may be safeguarded. Yet modern civilization is founded upon them. Without coal, oil and metals we should be shooting waterfowl and one another with bows and arrows —back fifty centuries.

But we could live without them. Deprived of the dynamic resources of land and water, we should be nonexistent. To philosophers who enjoy thinking in millenniums, it appears that western civilization is insecurely perched on a shelf of resources which are slowly but surely disintegrating.

When they are gone, humanity will have to resume its dependence on the self-renewing assets of forest, grass and water. The philosophers are undoubtedly correct, but the day of that dependence is far distant, and in the interim, if we can keep civilization together at all, scientists may evolve methods for securing adequate supplies of energy directly from the sun or for building raw materials from atomic bricks. If one is to think in millenniums, the curve of invention must also be taken into account.

For the next few decades, if not centuries, we must probably continue to rely on subsurface digging to provide metals and fuels for our automobiles, sewing machines, oil burners and electric refrigerators. During this period the question of the mineral supply and its possible exhaustion is of outstanding importance. No intelligent layman doubts this. But intelligent laymen have had so many awful warnings thundered upon their heads by Professor Doctor X, and so many optimistic contra notes, supported with curves and tables all complete, by Professor Doctor Y, that they are becoming confused. In this chapter we shall quote the professor doctors for what they may be worth—and some, I warn you, are very dependable—but before doing so, let us try to get the principles of mineral conservation in order. Here is something solid to fall back upon, even if all the charts and tables are ultimately found unreliable.

The first and most important principle is that resources are nothing but useless deposits until the standard of living admits them to a definite place on the table, as it were, and until the technical arts have advanced to the point where they may be obtained without an extravagant expenditure of labor. The discovery of a mountain of solid gold would not constitute an important addition to our resources, but only a glittering dump. It would convince even professors of classical economics that the gold standard was done for, while it would probably have little use in the arts, and would be much too heavy for kitchenware. "The material resources of the United States," says Charles A. Beard, "cannot be mathematically determined once and for all, and as Zimmerman has precisely stated the case, it is impossible to present a picture of resources until we have determined the kind of nation we want to create—made its standard of life budget."

The second principle is concerned with the factor of time. How much shall we dig today, and how much shall we reserve for our children and our children's children? If we dig too greedily, they will have nothing. If we conserve too thriftily, they will benefit unfairly at our expense. It goes without saying that, under the concept of infinity, Americans have dug and wasted on the candid principle, first enunciated by Uncle Joe Cannon: "What has posterity done for us?" Let the future worry. If now we are to become resource conscious, we need not leap to the other extreme and save just for the moral exhilaration of saving.

The third principle, or better, admonition, is to distinguish between the dollar cost of resources and their use-value down the years. A wild competitive scramble for oil may force the price down to ten cents a barrel. The consumer, with luck, gets ten-cent gasoline. Splendid. But in the turmoil oil fields are prematurely and wastefully exhausted, petroleum supplies begin to run low, and presently gasoline shoots to thirty cents, to forty cents. It would be better

194

for all concerned to pay higher prices to begin with and lower prices to end with. Oil would last longer and the average price to the consumer would be less. In looking at these resources we are dealing with geology. We must discount ephemeral money systems, adopt the physical frame of reference and think primarily in terms of human wants, available supply and time.

The fourth principle is that the total known supply of a given mineral means little without information about its availability. Vast coal and iron beds are said to be in the middle of the Amazonian jungle. Try to get them out; they might as well be on the moon. England has used only seven per cent of her coal reserves. Yet the mines are now so deep that costs are becoming prohibitive. Accessibility is often more important than richness of deposit.

A fifth principle is concerned with technical progress. An improvement in the method of burning coal which doubles the heat released automatically doubles coal reserves. Early conservationists of the Theodore Roosevelt school neglected this principle. When it was discovered that nitrogen could be taken from the air, conservation of nitrate deposits became a secondary matter.

A sixth principle is the establishment of a scale from abundance to scarcity. Such a scale would run approximately like this:

1. Superabundant minerals about which we need not worry, like sand, clay, abrasives, gravel, stone, cement, arsenic, aluminum clays, gypsum, salt, borax.

2. Minerals abundant enough to cause no immediate worries:

195

bituminous coal, low-grade iron ores, barite, fluor-spar, magnesite, molybdenum, potash and others.

3. Materials which are running thin and require care: anthracite, antimony, phosphate rock and others.

4. Scarce minerals which call for active conservation, such as petroleum, natural gas, copper, lead, zinc, mercury, tungsten, vanadium.

The above scale is for the United States. If we take North America as our base, the scale changes; if we take all American possessions, it changes again; if we take the world as a unit, it changes materially. National shortages are frequent, world shortages less common. Professor Ross A. Gartner points out, however, that the world has used up from one-tenth to one-half of its mineral resources in the last century. Tin is becoming scarce, yet we wrap it around cigarettes and candy.

World Resources

If we had intelligence enough to maintain a World Raw Material Control, many of the reasons for modern wars would evaporate and concern about minerals would be greatly lessened. Each nation would know that it would receive its fair share of the available world supply. Meanwhile the United States and Russia have far more resources within their own boundaries than other nations have. The British Empire can almost match them, but the empire depends on the navy and on long roads of transport. Brooks Emeny has identified nineteen minerals and three agricultural products as of paramount importance in war.

They are:

Coal	Bauxite	Antimony
Iron ore	Zinc	Tin
Petroleum	Manganese	Mercury
Copper	Nickel	Mica
Lead	Chromite	Cotton
Nitrates	Tungsten	Rubber
Sulphur	Potash	Wool
	Phosphates	

Let us note how well the seven great powers are supplied with these, including colonial possessions and regions of control, as well as home territory. (See the diagram on page 199.)

The *United States* is short of rubber and somewhat short of chromite, antimony and tin.

Russia is short of rubber, antimony, tin, tungsten, and is not too well provided with nickel and bauxite.

Great Britain (including the empire) is short of mercury, antimony and potash and needs more petroleum, sulphur, cotton and phosphate.

Germany needs petroleum, copper, cotton, bauxite, rubber, manganese, nickel, chromite, tungsten, wool, phosphates, antimony, tin, mercury, mica, and some lead, sulphur and zinc. Indeed all she is sure of are coal, iron, nitrates and potash. The reason for Hitler becomes plainer.

France requires petroleum, copper, cotton, zinc, rubber, tungsten, wool, tin, mercury, and some lead, sulphur, manganese, phosphate and mica. She is sure only of coal, iron, nitrates, bauxite, nickel, chromite, potash and antimony.

Italy is short of everything except iron, lead, nitrates, sulphur, bauxite, zinc and mercury. She is totally without petroleum,

197

cotton, rubber, nickel, chromite, tungsten, phosphate, tin and mica. The Ethiopian adventure becomes plainer.

Japan is short of everything but coal, iron, copper, nitrates, sulphur, chromite, tungsten and mica; she entirely lacks bauxite, rubber, nickel and wool. The invasion of Mongolia and China is rationalized if not defended.

Japan has none of the twenty-two essentials to export; Italy has sulphur, zinc and mercury; Russia, petroleum, manganese and tungsten; France, iron ore, bauxite and phosphate; Great Britain, coal and nitrates; Germany, coal, nitrates and potash. The United States exports coal, petroleum, copper, sulphur, cotton, zinc and phosphates.

America used to be totally dependent on Europe for potash. Drilling by the federal government in New Mexico, Utah and Texas has uncovered a supply sufficient to make us independent. Helium, which lifts dirigibles without danger of explosion, used to cost $2,500 a cubic foot. The government now makes it for one-half cent a cubic foot. A real search for minerals, conducted as the Russians are now conducting their surveys with every aid of science, would probably disclose additional supplies. Most of our minerals have been discovered by Cactus Pete with pack mule, spade, and a bundle of hunches and superstitions.

It is a common idea that world peace would be promoted if "sated" nations should divide up raw materials with "hungry" nations. Hoare used this argument in his precious compact with Laval for Ethiopian peace. Italy, Germany and Japan are the hungry ones; the United States, the British Empire and France are the sated. Too simple, says Jonathan

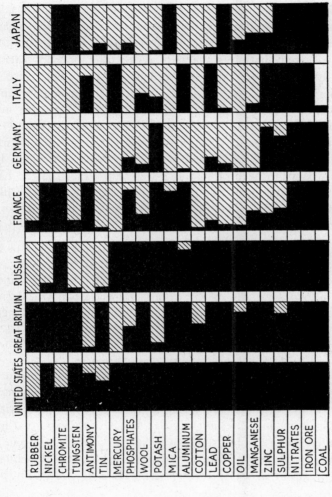

WAR TIME SELF-SUFFICIENCY **THE SEVEN GREAT POWERS** (including Colonial Possessions)

UNITED STATES · GREAT BRITAIN · RUSSIA · FRANCE · GERMANY · ITALY · JAPAN

RUBBER · NICKEL · CHROMITE · TUNGSTEN · ANTIMONY · TIN · MERCURY · PHOSPHATES · WOOL · POTASH · MICA · ALUMINUM · COTTON · LEAD · COPPER · OIL · MANGANESE · ZINC · SULPHUR · NITRATES · IRON ORE · COAL

Diagram 6.

199

Mitchell.* Nations, except Russia, do not sell raw materials; businessmen sell them. The businessmen are often organized into airtight international cartels. The local population of a "sated" nation is just as hungry as the local population of Italy or Japan. All are forced to pay the world price— take it or leave it. England and Holland dominate tin? Nonsense. The London Metals Exchange, a private monopoly, dominates tin. Sicily and Texas have a monopoly on brimstone sulphur. The private owners organized a tidy little cartel and proceeded to hold up Mussolini when he was badly in need of sulphur, despite the fact that he had lent the cartel some money. He paid through the nose like everybody else. The United States has no monopoly on bauxite; Andrew Mellon has it.

The wrath of the people of the hungry nations ought to be directed not toward England and other sated nations, but toward the relatively small group of businessmen who own the sources of many of the world's raw materials, and who are to some degree above and outside the control of governments. . . . Hungry people in every nation are exploited by sated owners.

Oil and Gas

Shortages in oil have been heralded for twenty years, and every warning has been answered with the discovery of new fields. I will present the latest, and I believe most authoritative alarm, but I refuse to guarantee it. I have burned my fingers before. This study was prepared by L. C. Snider and B. T. Brooks, and was published by the Chemical Foundation in 1935. It forecasts a shortage of oil in the

* *New Republic*, Jan. 8, 1936.

United States within five to eight years, namely, between 1940 and 1943. At that time we must begin either to import oil or to use substitutes. There will be no sudden extinction, as in the case of the passenger pigeon, but a slow decline, with rising costs. Some wells will go on pumping limited daily supplies for a generation. Riding through the Mississippi Valley, one sees many little pumps thumping away in cornfields, extracting the last dregs of an ancient pool, a barrel or two a day. It took from 1857, when the original well came in in Pennsylvania, to 1900 to produce the first billion barrels. Now we gallop through a billion barrels in about thirteen months.

Messrs Snider and Brooks admit cheerfully that all earlier estimates of shortage have failed to materialize and that the public is weary of cries of "Wolf, Wolf!" Today, however, more facts are available. Cactus Pete has given way to science. Prospecting is now better; instruments are greatly improved. Geophysics discovers the unseen. The known reserves total betweeen ten and thirteen billion barrels. Agreement on this figure is general. Wells are being pumped at 12,000 feet, an unheard-of depth. If no new fields are found and present consumption remains unaltered, oil will be gone mathematically in less than fifteen years. The mathematics is irrelevant. Shortage occurs when price begins to climb, when substitutes begin to creep in, when shale deposits are tapped as they already have been in Scotland, when stocks and bonds are floated for the hydro-genation of coal, as in Germany and England.

Since 1931 annual discoveries of new fields have averaged only 580 million barrels a year, while we need almost a billion to remain at par. The discovery curve reached its peak in the period between 1926 and 1930. No major field has come in since 1931. The percentage of dry holes is increasing; the national average is now above thirty per cent, in some states fifty per cent. "The available evidence indicates that we will be fortunate if we can supply our own consumption at its present rate for any period longer than five years, and a shortage may develop sooner should consumption increase." Schemes for increasing recovery from present fields—water flooding, sand pumping, open-pit mining—are not regarded by our authors as promising solutions for the whole problem. We have plenty of shale, but it costs the thrifty Scotch $3.02 a barrel to extract oil from local shale.

The most telling evidence of all is this: Nineteen companies own 91 per cent of all American reserves. These corporations are now intent on securing options on foreign sources. If there were "plenty of oil for an indefinite future," they would save their passage money. Oil-company executives see the handwriting on the wall.

The National Resources Board summarizes the chief wastes in the recovery of petroleum as follows:

1. Overcrowding of wells in flush producing areas and developing such fields faster than demand warrants. The state capitol of Oklahoma is now surrounded by a forest of derricks.

2. Operating fields with improper gas-oil ratios by blowing away the gas, which is essential to full recovery of petroleum. The heating value of gas wasted at Kettleman Hills in 1930 equalled the energy output of Boulder Dam for a year. In the Texas Panhandle gas has blown off at the rate of one billion cubic feet a day,

202

the equivalent of 40,000 tons of coal. An oil pool is a reservoir of energy. If the gas is vented, the energy balance breaks down and most of the oil stays forever underground.

3. Physical waste of gas at the surface.

4. Underground losses due to migration into strata where reclamation is impossible. The invasion of water into the oil sands.

5. Inefficient equipment.

6. Evaporation, leaks and fires in excessive storage facilities erected to meet competition.

7. The consumption of "distress" oil, forced on the market by overrapid development, for purposes for which other fuels should be used.

8. Price cutting due to flooding world markets with distress oil.

9. Premature abandonment of fields as the result of demoralized prices.

Van Hise estimates that for every barrel used five barrels are left forever unrecoverable underground.

It is interesting to note that the Dakota artesian basin, filled with water instead of petroleum, has suffered from many of the same wastes. It has been ruined by wild wells, leaks, careless drilling, uncontrolled gushers and the release of pressure.

Underground fluids like oil and water have no respect for property rights. They refuse to recognize their lawful owners. They thumb their noses at learned judges. Oil is supposed to be kept in line by the "law of capture," which comes down from earlier days before petroleum wells were known. This law holds that the owner of surface land above the pool is entitled to all the oil he can get from

203

his well and that the property owner on the adjoining lot must not interfere. "It was believed," says Governor Marland of Oklahoma, "that oil flowed underground like a river. We know now that oil doesn't flow, and that wells drain neighboring land, but our courts accepted the old Pennsylvania law and the fellow with neighboring land has no rights."

The fluid nature of petroleum, gas and water makes them move toward a region of lower pressure. The law of capture gives surface possession. Under the prevailing leasing system, the lessee is often forced to drill to retain his rights. He must produce in order to fulfill the royalty contract, even though the market is already flooded. Agreements for joint exploitation of the whole pool would be fairer but they are shunned for fear of antitrust laws. Between the Sherman Act and the law of capture, a high premium is placed upon waste and financial demoralization. When the more progressive oil men try to take steps in the direction of conservation, the "hot-oil" gentry wreck their program. The laws of property and the laws of geology run at right angles, and the resources of the continent pay the cost. "Texas is much less concerned about the future oil supply of the United States than she is lest Oklahoma or Louisiana be permitted to drill faster than she."

In Denmark, when deposits of oil or other minerals are discovered, they automatically become the property of the state. The community may then lease them to private citizens, but only on condition that the laws of geology are duly respected. There will be fantastic waste in America until an oil pool is exploited as a unit, with no more holes thrust into it than gas and migration conditions warrant. If there is more than one owner above, let all owners share equitably in the proceeds of the whole pool. As the pools of this country draw toward their historic close, and as petroleum becomes increasingly scarce, it is clear that only the community can be trusted with its exploitation. The production of oil—not necessarily the refining and selling—must be rigorously controlled by the government.

Coal

At last accounts our deposits of coal are good for the next 4,000 years. So we may forget it as a resource problem? Not quite. Anthracite will not last so long as that. It is already one-quarter gone. Average working depths in Pennsylvania have increased 77 per cent in recent years; seams are barely half as thick as they used to be. "Anthra-cite, semibituminous or smokeless coal, and the coking coals," says Fred G. Tryon, who, if anybody, should know, "are being exhausted very rapidly and sooner or later we will have to face the problem of finding substitutes for them."

The coal industry is scandalously operated. The Guffey coal bill was not a bright idea of the government to pester business, but an answer to a plea from a very sick industry. Excessive competition has ruined its financial health. In western Europe the average avoidable waste runs from five to ten per cent; in the United States thirty-five per cent, or 150 million tons, has been thrown away in a year. The industry has been in the doldrums since the war. In the peak year of 1929, 1,437 companies, producing about half the national tonnage, operated at a loss. Aggregate losses for the whole industry exceeded profits. The depression made a bad matter worse. For the last seven years, one-third of the coal miners of this country have been completely idle, wasting their lives away in black slums on bleak hills. The companies have been forced to skim the cream to keep going at all, working only the richer seams. Efficient concerns that used to recover 85 per cent are now obtaining only 60 per cent, according to the National Resources Board. From 1923 to 1932, 4,802 mines were shut down or abandoned, most of them with plenty of coal down below. Once abandoned, a mine is almost impossible to open again. Water comes in, mine timbers cave, the whole working becomes a death trap, like the old Nova Scotia gold mine where three men were caught while the world breathlessly awaited their rescue. Hundreds of millions of tons of coal have been sealed off forever. "Were these abandoned mines in Belgium, the loss would be regarded as a national calamity." Not only is the mine wrecked, but sometimes the surface of the land above it. "Johnston City, Illinois, already crippled economically by the flooding of its principal coal mine, faced a new menace today after a land fault over an abandoned mine moved houses from their foundations, broke a city gas main and cracked pavements in the streets."*

The fat rich seams are not what they were. The glories of the Moshannon bed are but a memory. Only a few acres remain of the Big Vein in George's Creek. Pocahontas and New River have been deeply mined. The case of England is instructive. Up to 1850 she led the world in producing

* Associated Press dispatch, Mar. 25, 1936.

coal, iron, copper, lead, zinc and tin. None of these ores is exhausted, or will be for decades, if ever. *But the reserves are too costly to get at.* Copper mining has all but ceased, lead production is small, tin declines. Only seven per cent of British coal is gone, but mines are down 3,700 feet, working on fourteen-inch seams. To get a ton to the surface costs 1.7 man-hours in the United States, but 7.5 man hours in England. Mining difficulties in that country have long since absorbed the gains of technology. Output per man-hour has been falling since the '80's. Here is an ominous warning for us in America.

Copper

The mining of copper is plagued with the same excess capacity that bedevils coal. The industry was equipped to produce a million tons a year and in 1933 production was less than 200,000 tons, twenty per cent of capacity. Sixty-five thousand miners had shrunk to 16,000. Operators were forced to disregard the most elementary work of maintenance. They could afford to take only the cream—"picking the eyes out," to use the miners' term. Pillars are pulled, caving old stopes. Shafts and main haulage ways collapse. Barren rock and good ore are crushed together, at present unreclaimable. Water climbs up the workings. To reopen an abandoned copper mine—if possible at all—costs twice as much as to sink a new mine. Meanwhile, mining towns go bankrupt, financially and humanly. In arid regions the very water supply may vanish when the mine closes. Houghton, Hancock, Butte and Globe are ghost towns, according to the National Resources Board. "As the water creeps up the Michigan copper mines, the community dies." Michigan mines are a mile deep, the deepest in the world.

The situation is the more serious because copper is a critical resource. Only fifteen million* more tons are available at reasonable working costs. At the 1927 output, this means fifteen years, but, as in England, the condition of shortage will develop long before the physical end comes. In 1932 a tariff was placed on copper, the telltale sign that the metal approaches the shortage point. Whenever you see a duty imposed for the first time upon a mineral mined at home, you may be almost sure that it is the red flag of coming exhaustion.

Other Minerals

Lead is in the same precarious situation as copper. Its output before the depression was nearly 700,000 tons a year; the 1933 production was 273,000 tons, a decline of 60 per cent. Fourteen thousand miners lost their jobs. The eyes were picked out of the richest veins and workings were ruined. There have been no new discoveries of lead for twenty years. The available reserves are estimated at ten million tons, which will last fifteen years more at the 1929 production rate.

Zinc follows an identical pattern. New deposits have recently been located in Mexico, Canada, Spain and Australia, but not in the United States. In 1933 only one-third of zinc retorts were utilized. The war demand caused the farmers who owned shallow deposits of zinc to drop the plow

* Other estimates run as high as 30,000,000 tons. I am following the National Resources Board.

and take up the shovel. Scores of little mines were opened. Low prices closed these mines and the ore was lost through water seepage. In other areas "all mines are now flooded." Reserves are placed at eleven to twelve million tons—say fifteen to twenty years more at the predepression rate.

Gold production passed its peak in 1915. Silver is on the decline, and no more Comstock Lodes or Leadvilles are in sight. Mesabi iron is half gone since 1893, with perhaps another forty years to go. Behind that remain plenty of ores of a lower grade, which means higher man-hour cost. Mercury has passed its peak. Vanadium is given ten to fifteen years more, tungsten about eight years at the 1926 rate.

Of thirty-three metal-mining districts which have yielded great wealth, only five have been discovered since 1900, and none at all since 1907. Today 63 per cent of all our mineral production is behind the telltale tariff wall. "The handicaps of thinner beds, leaner ores and growing depth are beginning to be felt. The problem of conservation is not to prepare for a day centuries hence when all the fuel and metal shall be gone, but to minimize the readjustment to a stage of increasing cost which in older lands has already arrived."

The insane waste of abandoned mines and workings should be stopped. If individual owners cannot stop it, the community must. Copper, lead and zinc are of vital importance and shortage is indicated, not within the lifetime of our children, but within our own. Wastes in refining and utilization must be reduced. The use of scrap is a major method of conservation. Old motorcars should be lifted out

209

of the dumps which now make the countryside hideous, and their metals should be returned to the smelters through the scrap market. For every ton of coal burned there is a ton less to burn, but for every ton of iron, copper, lead or zinc used there can be half a ton or more to use again. Some industries subsist entirely on scrap. Today more scrap is used in copper production than new metal. Poking around the harbors of the world, one finds rusty tramp steamers, flying the Japanese flag, filling their holds with scrap metals which other nations are too lazy or too stupid to save. The United States, facing shortages, goes blithely ahead exporting scrap. "The subject of scrap is the great blind spot of the world's metal economy."

Swedish Steel

In Sweden the state owns all mineral rights. In the north, within the Arctic Circle, are vast deposits of iron ore. These are leased to a corporation called the K. L. B., of which half the shares are owned by the government and half by private capital. The state receives:

1. A royalty on every ton mined, as owner of the deposit.
2. Dividends on its K. L. B. stock.
3. Traffic on the state railroads, which are very profitable despite the low rates charged. The profit has been used to electrify the lines.

Towns in the mining region tax the K. L. B. and the proceeds are employed to construct model mining communities. Kiruna houses 1,800 miners and operates libraries, public baths, gymnasiums, lecture, courses and concerts. Every miner's house is electrified, and many are heated by electricity. Arctic Circle temperatures demand a lot of heat. This shows what cheap power can do. Coming up from the mine at the end of a shift, a miner rides to town on the free municipal trolley line, leaves his clothes in a locker at the public baths, takes a shower, steam bath and ultra-violet bath and puts on fresh clothes for home. Schools and dental and medical attention are all free, with hot lunches for the school children. Trade schools are free. Yet the K. L. B. makes a good profit.* I hope some miner in Butte, Montana, reads these words. They will show him that the hell he has endured is not in the inexorable nature of things, but is only plain stupidity mixed with the methods of Anaconda.

Minerals and Land

Finally we must examine the important cross link between minerals and land, between dead resources and living. The land must have nitrogen, phosphorus and potassium, especially phosphorus. How does the supply of these three major plant foods hold out? Nitrogen is still imported from Chile, but we have discovered how to take it from the air. If enough cheap power is available, nitrogen presents no problem. It can also be obtained by planting beans, peas and vetches, which fix nitrogen through their root bacteria. There is no serious problem here.

Potassium once came from German deposits at Stassfurt. The Bureau of Mines has developed a process to grind

---

* Marquis W. Childs: *Sweden, the Middle Way.* Yale University Press, 1936.

211

potash rock—sylvite and polyhalite. A billion tons of this rock has been found in Wyoming, with more deposits in Texas and New Mexico. The government has the supply in charge and we do not need to worry about potassium.

Phosphorus, according to Dr. H. A. Morgan of the TVA, is the critical resource. Generation after generation of men and animals have eaten phosphorus out of the soil, and the bones it once built lie segregated in ten thousand grave-yards. The packinghouses return a small amount. The main source of supply is a series of deposits of fossilized bones and shells of prehistoric animals lying in the rocks. Such deposits occur in Tennessee, Florida and the Rocky Mountains—most of them in the Rockies, thus requiring a long freight haul. According to Dr. Morgan, we need every pound to bring our soils back to par. Meanwhile phosphate rock is being mined and exported in large quantities, especially to Japan. This in his opinion is a national crime—like shipping foodstuffs for profit out of a hungry country. The best wines contain the most phosphorus. A French chemist named Paturel has shown that, when vintages for different years are arranged in order of P_2O_5 content, the sequence is almost identical with the order of excellence assigned by wine merchants.

In March, 1936, I was in Knoxville. One morning Dr. Morgan seized me by the arm and pushed me into a car, his eyes blazing with excitement. We drove out to a gently sloping field on the experimental farm of the University of Tennessee. It was raining softly and spring was in the air. Here in neat squares, perhaps twenty feet to a side,

212

were twenty-seven green plots of winter wheat pushing through the red earth. Nine of them were "control" plots, fed with nitrogen and potassium but no phosphorus. Nine had been fed with standard commercial phosphate. The remaining nine had received—for the first time in history— a new low-cost phosphate developed by Dr. Morgan in the electric furnaces at Muscle Shoals. The control plots were easy to recognize, poor and thin beside the vivid green of the other eighteen. Could I distinguish between the standard phosphate and the new? I could not. Sometimes I guessed one and sometimes the other. There was no visible difference.

This meant that the new phosphate nourished wheat as well as the old, although it could be produced at perhaps one-quarter of the cost. It is called *calcium metaphosphate* and runs some 63 per cent pure element. This particular experiment was to determine whether nature under normal field conditions would accept the new phosphate. In glass beakers in the university laboratory the case appeared doubtful. Here was conclusive answer in the springing wheat. Dr. Morgan's face was illuminated. He saw the continent drinking in the new material, coming back to health after generations of progressive soil starvation. I looked over the curve of the hill to the Great Smokies beyond and wondered if I were witness to one of the most important days in American history.

"Dams, yes," says Dr. H. A. (like all good American executives, the Big Shots of the TVA are known by their initials), "dams are good. But if we could raise the underground water table of the Tennessee Valley only six inches,

213

that would mean four times as much water as Norris reservoir will hold.* Nature would do the storing."

Storage of this kind depends on cover crops of forest and grass, especially grass. Cover crops require fertilizers to receive their start, especially phosphorus. The phosphorus may presently be ready to ship at an unheard-of economy. The Great Wheel turns.

* The whole valley covers twenty-six million acres. A six-inch increase in water table equals thirteen million acre-feet. Norris reservoir holds 3,350,000 acre-feet.

Chapter XIII

THE RESOURCE BASE

THE situation we have described is a little like a family moving into a fine, big, well-furnished house. There is room for everybody, with all the comforts and conveniences. But no provision has been made for fuel. Food must be cooked and the big house heated. So the family begins to burn the house down, piece by piece. First the beds, chairs and bureaus, then the doors and partitions. Up come the floor boards. Finally they start on the studs and beams and roof. It will not be long now before the family is out in the cold.

One continental resource after another has been devastated. The beaver went first. The trappers eliminated him in short order. Then the forests, the tobacco soils of Virginia, the tall grass, the short grass, the soils of the cotton belt, the passenger pigeon, the Rio Grande region, gold and silver, the buffalo and the antelope, the best of the artesian basins, petroleum and natural gas, watershed after watershed, game and waterfowl, the marsh lands, copper, lead and zinc, the salmon and the sturgeon.

Each assault made money for somebody at the time, and so kept the national house warm. Each has been hailed by red-faced gentlemen in silk hats on flag-draped rostrums as progress, enlightenment and the realization of the American dream. Many have been accompanied by issues of stocks, bonds, mortgages, checks, currency and great activity in Wall Street. The Great Plains beef boom attracted capital from all over the world. Financial fires have roared; land values have soared; mortgages have topped the Rockies; bankers have looked benevolently over their wing collars and declared everything sound. And all the time the fundamental curves have taken this course:

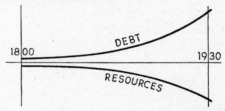

Debt has gone up at a compound interest rate of around five per cent for the last hundred years, while resources—especially soil, forest, grass and oil—have gone down. Declining resources, however, have resulted in greater physical production, for the time being. In 1910 or thereabouts, according to Bassett Jones, the *rate* of production (not production itself) began to decline, giving the following generalized curve:

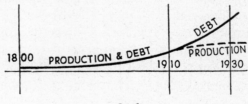

216

The above two diagrams tell the story. Up to 1910 or so, physical production grew as fast as debt, and standards of living rose. Then production began to level off as resources were depleted, but debt continued upward at the old rate. The situation becomes increasingly fantastic. The depression halted the expansion of debt a little, but the Reconstruction Finance Corporation, the Farm Credit Authority and the Home Owners Loan Corporation bolstered the structure with government loans.

America has achieved its relatively high standards by living on its resource capital, by taking more out of the continent than was put back. This was and is inevitable for mineral resources underground, but it is the road to ruin for land and water resources. It was a tightrope act which delighted the spectators while it lasted, but the rope was too long, and the performers are beginning to hit the ground.

What a dramatic picture it all presents! The fringe of settlements on the Atlantic seaboard. The files of dusty travelers making their way west through the notches in the Appalachians—on foot, on horseback, in wagons. Flat boats up the Mississippi, and flat boats down from the Great Lakes, laden with settlers. Clipper ships around the Horn to California, and the invasion east into the Great Basin. The golden spike which joined the first transcontinental railroad in 1867. The branch rail lines, sprouting like twigs from a stem and covering the map. The steady stream of ships from Europe—Ellis Island, then off to claim a home-stead near cousin Oscar in Minnesota. The flash of axes,

217

the scream of rock drills, the ripping of the prairie sod. A gray sweaty stream of humanity pouring over every mountain pass, penetrating every valley, examining almost every stone, tumbling into one rich resource pocket after another, until there were no more pockets.

Room for all, work for all, opportunity for most, great fortunes for the lucky. Population growing as fast as debt and physical production. Rising prices, new inventions, the colossal network of transport to be laid down, expanding foreign trade, the gold rush, the beef boom, the Civil War boom, the oil boom, the steel boom, the wheat boom, the World War triple boom, the Hollywood boom, the Florida boom, the motorcar and highway boom, installment selling, bank-credit inflation and the stock market lustily discounting rosy expectations for an indefinitely expanding future.

To sell America short was the crime of crimes. To believe that Jonesville was not the busiest, livest, fastest growing little town in the state and that its population (actual, 5,000; chamber of commerce, 10,000) was not destined to reach 100,000 in a decade was high treason. In the excitement, no one saw—or if he did, he refused to credit his eyes —that resource pocket after pocket had become exhausted. It took the grim reality of the depression, when even local chambers of commerce came down to earth, to disclose the tragedy which had been gathering for a long time.

See them come—men, women and children—an army millions strong, with tired eyes and bent heads. They have worked hard, swung the axes, plowed the grasslands, irrigated the desert, drained the marshes, paved the roads, supported the schools, tried the best they knew. And the

218

good earth has gone out from under; the continent has no more to give.

Blighted Areas

In the foregoing chapters we have mentioned various exhausted resource areas. Let us bring them together:

1. *Crop-land Areas.*—100 million acres of once-fertile soil are now eroded beyond hope for livelihood. Other large acreages of soil are depleted, with plant food gone through crop mining. The cotton belt is sinking as a result of one-crop farming and the decline of foreign markets.

2. *Grassland Areas.*—165 million acres are on the way to ruin through overgrazing, fire, the plow, dust and drought. The carrying capacity of grass lands has declined forty to fifty per cent.

3. *Forest-land Areas.*—We have eighty-three million acres of lifeless land and stranded forest communities with merchantable trees gone.

4. *Watershed Areas.*—Here we remember dying irrigation projects, the survivors of unsuccessful drainage projects, the Wisconsin and Minnesota peat marshes, the blasted Rio Grande. The delta of the Central Valley is invaded by salt water. The artesian basins sink. Some regions have been made uninhabitable by pollution. Flood victims try to exist on a score of rivers, with their source of livelihood permanently washed away.

5. *Wild-life Areas.*—The picture shows stricken fishing villages and hunting, trapping and fur communities. It shows the decline of towns once dependent on the run and canning of salmon. It shows Nantucket before fishermen organized to hold their resource.

6. *Mining Areas.*—Copper towns, lead towns, zinc towns, oil towns. Miners on the margin suffer more than marginal farmers. Wheat lands can often go back to grass or other uses, but nothing

but copper and profanity comes out of a copper mine. A cotton farmer can sometimes look about for another crop, but a zinc miner is left up in the mountains, often with no water supply. Of stranded miners in Utah, the National Resources Board says: "The condition of these men and their families is perhaps the most tragic of any group of American workers."

In the winter of 1935–1936, 1,400,000 rural families were on relief. W. W. Alexander of the Resettlement Administration classes them into victims of falling farm prices after the 1929 smash and victims of chronic maladjustments due chiefly to failing resources. The first group can climb out if farm prices rise high enough. Without collective aid the second group is lost. In addition, Mr. Alexander finds 500,-000 rural families not technically on relief who have been accepted for rehabilitation—meaning loans, farm animals, machinery, tools, seeds, assistance in farm management. These families are found largely in the drought and dust-storm areas and are being assisted to rehabilitate their own homes.

On June 28, 1934, the passage of the Taylor Grazing Act ended a long chapter in American history. It closed the public domain to further entry by homesteaders and buried a policy which had been slowly dying. The peak was in 1862 when Lincoln signed the Homestead Act, which gave 160 acres of virgin land free to any qualified settler. Free land is a strong American tradition. Political parties like the Free Soil Party of 1850 have battled for it. The aristocratic Virginia colony joined the revolutionists—low fellows she thought them—because, for one reason, she needed virgin soil to replace her exhausted tobacco fields. According

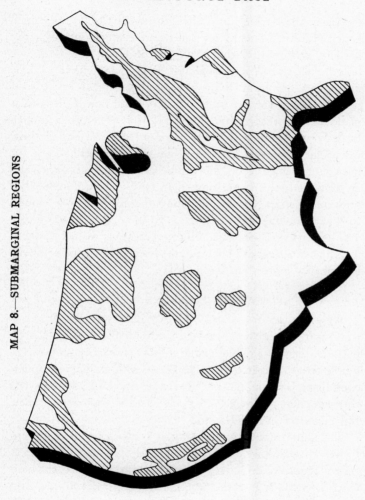

MAP 8.—SUBMARGINAL REGIONS

221

to Beard, the Republican Party got its start by a deal which gave western farmers free land and eastern interests the banking system and the tariff. In the Great Plains, as we noted earlier, 160 acres was not enough for either a cattle ranch or a dry farm. Even 640 acres, granted in 1916, was not enough in the dry cycle. "Every time a new entry was made in the records of the Land Office, another human tragedy was launched." The Taylor Act has ended these particular tragedies. Cattle owners may still take out licenses for grazing on the public domain—just as licenses are obtained for cutting timber in the National Forest—but now *under strict supervision*. The number of cattle is limited to what the grass can carry.

The map is stained with blighted areas, as the accompanying illustration shows. The number of Americans involved is probably more than ten million.

The Concept of Infinity

Why has this happened? The socialists will instantly cite the capitalist system, rugged individualism, the lack of national planning. This is true in part, but it cannot be the whole truth. Other nations have enjoyed, or suffered under, capitalism, as you please, but have not so ruthlessly run through their resources. Look at Germany, Sweden, France, Italy, Austria, New Zealand.

The major reason, in my opinion, is the concept of infinity to which we have so often referred. No other nation— except Russia and China—ever had such a slice of continent to play with. No other nation, including Russia, ever had such wealth in resources. Looking from the Atlantic to the fabulous Pacific, there seemed no end. What if a forest was leveled here or a field gullied there? Move on, brother, move on; the great open spaces beckon. It is this concept which inspires the chamber of commerce, the boosters, the boomers, Wall Street itself. It is this spirit which looks confidently for the corner to be turned, the corner which has always been there. Even today, after seven years of unprecedented depression, businessmen, farmers, labor, Main Street, are still largely intolerant of any suggestion that an epoch has ended, that the boy has grown up and must begin to pay his own bills.

Other nations, because of their smaller size or more limited primeval heritage, or because of plain common sense, have dreamed no dreams of a land which stretches west to infinity. They early recognized that the ocean or Gaul lay over the ranges and that that was the end. Sweden began to preserve her forests in 1600.

If to the concept of infinity be added the usual practices of a reasonably ruthless capitalism and certain extraordinary property laws exclusively American, we come close to the true answer to the question why ten million citizens are without a resource base.

There is a law of growth, to quote Arthur L. Pollard, for a fruit fly, a pumpkin, an industry and a society. Social growth depends primarily on population, land area and production, of which population is the most important. The American population curve is leveling off like that of physical production. The maximum may not exceed 136 million, to be reached in 1955, followed by a slow decline.* Physical

* Thompson and Whelpton. O. E. Baker puts the peak earlier and lower.

production, as we noted earlier, is growing at a decrement. Crop area began to shrink thirty years ago. Thus the growth rate of all three major factors is declining. Remember, I said *rate*, not total quantity. Our population is getting older. In 1936 the age group from five to nineteen years will decrease by 200,000 while the group over sixty will increase by 400,000. One need not look farther to explain the strength of the Townsend old-age pension plan.

New York City is in the east and is thought to lack the exuberance of the west. Yet, according to Frederick L. Ackerman, the city has been zoned to restrict its growth so that its buildings cannot in the future accommodate more than 420 million persons. This in plain terms means that the zoners took the sky as the limit. The zoning ordinance has been solemnly sustained by judicial decision, accepted as a measure of population expectancy, used as a basis for appraisals and assessed valuations, and so has become the foundation for urban mortgages and funded debt.*

This is entirely typical. An American businessman expects to see his sales compound year by year with the same calm assurance with which he expects the sun to rise. Yet not only are population, production and crop area leveling off, but foreign trade is at a standstill, owing to economic nationalism, and excess plant capacity threatens nearly every major industry. Kilowatt-hours steadily replace man-hours and check industrial pay-rolls and buying power. Investment in private industry no longer absorbs savings. According to the Brookings Institution, it did not absorb them in the 1920's. The interest rate falls to unheard-of

* *New York Times*, June 21, 1936.

lows. Ruin and revolution? Not necessarily, but strong evidence that the American economy is maturing and must
adapt itself to a new set of growth curves, where a com-
pounding increase gives way to a modest regular increase, or
in some cases to no increase at all.

Those who lean up against the analogy of history and
bid us contemplate the recovery after 1873, 1893 and 1907
neglect these changes and growth factors. They cannot
distinguish an epoch from an episode. "Individuals who
behave as though they were perpetually young are merely
ridiculous, but societies which do the same are quite likely
to destroy themselves."

Speculation

The ideal of American farm tenure under the homestead
acts was the widest possible diffusion of owner operation.
The land was to be primarily for use rather than sale. The
self-interest of the owner, it was believed, would automatically secure for society the goods and services it needed,
and would thus square with the laissez-faire doctrine of
Adam Smith. The policy has not worked, says the National
Resources Board, because of land speculation, indifferent
land use, and tenant rather than owner operation.

Speculation has been a plague since 1630. It includes three
varieties: the holding of property for a rise in price, the
activity of land companies and "developers" out for a quick
turn, and mass speculation when the whole country goes
crazy, as in Iowa farm lands in 1920 and in Florida in 1925.
Speculation causes an owner to think more of selling out
than of conserving his land. It makes land costs unduly high

and reduces funds available for equipment and fertilizer. It increases the burden of debt and sharpens the struggle to meet interest and taxes. When farm-land values fall, as they did so disastrously after the war, the debt burden becomes intolerable. Sometimes the face of the mortgage exceeds the whole value of the farm.

The New Jersey State Planning Board finds "that a considerable portion of inferior farm land is kept in use through a practice termed 'sucker-baiting'—repeated sales of unproductive lands to inexperienced farmers from near-by cities. The spotty character of New Jersey soils, with poor land scattered deceptively through good, tends to facilitate such unscrupulous activities." Out come a crop of wistful white-collar would-be farmers from New York, Philadelphia and Newark, to pay the speculators their fat commissions, go bankrupt on poor soil, and so give way to the next crop of suckers. Land must be surveyed and zoned to stop the merry-go-round. The Florida Planning Board prays that the Everglades will be kept under water until there is a definite planned demand for more crop land. Otherwise the area, one of the last great bird refuges, will be wrecked by fire, oxidation, subsistence farming and speculators. The cut-over lands of northern Wisconsin were ballyhooed by speculators. Suckers streamed in to lose everything they owned on soil which was adapted only to forest.

Banks have frequently encouraged speculation. For a time they profited greatly at the expense of their farmer clients, but in the end they went down with them. The major evil was failure to appraise land on the basis of average yield over a series of years. Banks permitted their clients to pay more for land than it was worth, with prices temporarily boosted by virgin-soil conditions or by a wet cycle. With depletion or drought, values collapsed. The bank foreclosed and took the farm, to sell it in the next upswing at a fine profit. Sometimes one farm would thus be sold four or five times.

Tenantry

In the early days of this republic we pointed with scorn to the tenant-ridden countries of Europe. In America every man could sit under his own vine and fig tree. There was consternation when the census of 1880 revealed that one-quarter of all farmers had become tenants in spite of home-stead acts and liberal land laws. Arthur Young said in a famous statement that an owner's self-interest would prompt him to convert a desert into a garden, but give him a nine-year lease on a garden and he would reduce it to a desert. By 1930, 431 million acres, forty-four per cent of total farm acreage (including pasture and woodlot) were under lease; fifty-three per cent of all farmers operated some leased land; forty-two per cent leased all the land they worked. Thus nearly half had no vine and fig tree to call their own.

When the tenant is a relative of the owner, or hopes to become the owner soon, land is often conserved. If he has no hope, land runs down the gullies. One-seventh of all farm tenants are negroes. When cash rent prevails, the absentee landlord opposes all taxes and other charges, for he is interested solely in maximum exploitation of his property. Temporary ownership is unstable; "it means a sale psychology and not a use-and-conservation attitude toward the soil."

Thus the manner in which land has been held in America has put a premium on wasting soil, grass and forest. If the original policy of owner operation could have been enforced, the story might have been different. I doubt if it would have saved the continent, however, because the concept of infinity would have remained. The owner might prefer to run through his land and move west. Many, as a matter of fact, did just that. In France, farmer owners realize there is no golden west. They stay in the ancestral home and help nature build the soil.

Property

Our land laws come down from English common law where title was vested in the Crown. By grants of personal privileges, lords held of the king and tenants held of their lords. There was a personal obligation throughout the system. The king was the symbol for the nation, and abuse of land by lord or tenant was an affront to the Crown. Not until the time of Henry II could a tenant sell the land he worked. When the common law crossed to America, sovereign state supplanted crown. While in legal theory absolute right of property was vested in the state, practically the state reserved only three rights: the power to tax, eminent domain and police power—restraining the owner from committing certain public nuisances, like keeping a pigpen on Fifth Avenue.

Property is inconceivable without government. Otherwise one has to build oneself a castle and hire a private army like Mr. Hearst. But despite the fact that government and government alone makes private property possible, American practice, stoutly supported by court decisions, did not allow the government to prescribe rules of use. An owner had virtually complete right to use or abuse his land as he saw fit, limited only by the somewhat vague provisions of the police power.

Meanwhile, even if an owner desired to conserve his property, competitive conditions were often such that he could not do so. In an era of competitive logging and devastating fires, a lumberman who adopted permanent-yield forestry would promptly lose his markets to less scrupulous competitors. Again, taxes and interest on standing timber literally forced him to hasty cutting; he could not afford to wait. Farmers who saved their soil were often caught in the same vise. As a class, farmers hate soil mining. They want to keep land healthy. "But what choice have they," says Secretary Wallace, "when low prices and high fixed charges compel them to put in more and more acreage in order to produce enough to meet taxes and interest?"

A manufacturer who figures his costs with no allowance for depreciation can readily undersell his competitors. If all were forced to follow his cost-accounting methods, consumers would be pleased—until the sheriff took over the entire industry. That is precisely what lumbermen, farmers and cattlemen have done with the continental capital. It is highly dubious, furthermore, whether consumers have benefited much, because of the fabulous wastes involved.

The princely grants of alternate sections along the right of way made to the railroads have proved another source of land abuse. The carriers were not interested in planting vines and fig trees, but in what they could get out of it in cash. The grants were pied on the map with federal, state and private lands and "remain to this day a handicap to the effective use of range lands in the west."

When the law of property approached oil pools, artesian basins, declining water tables under groups of states, silting and wash on downstream lands, floods and pollution below, its operation was not only vicious but absurd. Such matters cannot be settled under narrow concepts of property because they transcend fixed boundaries. We remember the California downstream riparian owners who grow nothing but "nuisance values." These joint problems used to be matters for the Crown. They must become matters for the sovereign state; otherwise no individual owner has reasonable protection.

Handout

Conservatives bitterly protest government spending for relief and point with horror to the sums involved, calling it a largesse without precedent in history. They do not read much history. If they did, they would realize that the Roosevelt dole was very small change. The United States government in its time has given away not airy dollars but a good part of a solid continent—a dole of more than one billion acres of land.

William the Conqueror did not parcel out the Saxon holdings with any more lavish hand to his retainers than our government distributed those of the Indians. The Norman king made his awards on the basis of services rendered, and imposed conditions of tenure and responsibility which eventually made the English landed class acutely conscious of its duty to society. We have passed out titles of ownership without assigning obligation in the same measure, and without regard to the final good of all. The paternalism was that of a weak and indulgent parent, moved by present clamor rather than by any sense of future results. It is the children of just such parents who have to be restrained with violence when they become adults.*

There has been no real land policy in America. Until the present Roosevelt administration there was no careful and scientific classification of the public domain. The ease of acquisition led not only to speculation and monopoly but to downright fraud, where the hardy pioneer was merely a dummy, planted by commercial interests for the purpose of securing title to public lands. The idea—one cannot call it a policy—was to rid the republic of all responsibility for the public domain as rapidly as possible.

What a domain it was! The whole of the United States except the thirteen original colonies and Texas, first owned by the government, then given away. Some poor land was retained. The gifts occasionally netted a small fee to the government. The attitude of the recipients has been that not only were the gifts strictly in order, but they should carry no strings in the sense of supervised land and water use. An inalienable property right to perpetuity has been taken for granted. Now, as the blighted areas expand, the government is buying back its original largesse in a decidedly moth-eaten condition, at very substantial figures per acre. Upward of fifty million acres has reverted to local govern-

* Paul Sears: *Deserts on the March*. University of Oklahoma Press, 1935.

ments through tax delinquency, while more is coming back every day. Land tax delinquency alone is all the proof one needs of the ominous extent of blighted areas.

Business Enterprise

Agriculture, as Zimmerman points out, does not fit readily into normal business enterprise. Here is another reason why the farmer, on the defensive against the middle-man, has mined the soil. Agriculture uses "free goods"— sunshine, air, rain and snow. Its time cycle of production is beyond human control. Heaven knows—and I mean Heaven —when the harvest will ripen, or indeed if there will be any harvest at all. Farming requires huge storage facilities, but does not yield the capital necessary to finance such storage and marketing facilities. So quick-thinking men from Chicago, chewing stumps of cigars, arrange the facilities.

The farmer can guarantee neither quantity nor quality. One Ford V-8 is like another to the ten-thousandth of an inch; not so squashes. If motorcars were like corn and squashes, Mr. Ford would turn out 100 per cent perfect cars on Monday and 90 per cent rejects on Tuesday. A few Tuesdays and Mr. Ford would be ruined. When prices fall, the farmer produces more. When prices are threatened, big business, on the contrary, produces less and holds the price. The triple A—do not forget this—was an attempt to give agriculture some of the benefits of big business by restricting production and maintaining prices.

Indeed, capitalism in its phase of active competition is an enemy of the continent. The buyer craves abundance, the seller scarcity. Sellers with a stock in hand like to see natural

232

PLATE X.—DUST STORM. (*Photo by Acme.*)

catastrophes which encourage scarcity—boll weevils, floods, fires, dust storms, hurricanes. When drought smites the wheat lands, prices go happily up on the Chicago Exchange; when it rains, they go down. The extent of buoyancy measures the extent of the catastrophe. The floods of the spring of 1936 were a matter of congratulation among circles dealing in railroad bridges, structural steel, cement, lumber, rowboats and hospital supplies. This may be good for business—at least somebody's business—but it is very bad for the continent. From the point of view of ethics, I should prefer to take lessons from a cage of cobras. The fortunes of lumber tycoons and other great exploiters have been defended on the plea that, after all, even if they were hard and merciless men, they built up the country. What they really did was to tear the continent down.

Hot Oil

Why have American resources not been safeguarded? We have given many reasons, but it may be well to end with a specific one. It is perhaps an extreme case, but it reflects a mood which has been in evidence since the beginning.

In the east Texas hot-oil country, one sees thousands of flares at night, rising at the tips of iron pipes. The pipes are high as a house, and the flames as high again. The roaring flares turn night into day. They are fed by natural gas, while operators below frantically pump bootleg oil. Production is in violation of both state and federal law.

Secretary Wilbur, under President Hoover, inaugurated the first restrictions on this practice in an attempt to conserve oil. Alfalfa Bill Murray of Oklahoma called out the militia in a further attempt, but the American dream was not to be gainsaid. Oil in recent months (1935) has been selling around one dollar a barrel, which means fifteen-cent gasoline. Hot oil is profitable at fifty cents a barrel, allowing ten-cent gasoline. East Texas is replete with small owners, eager to take advantage of this situation.

East Texas is a desolate region, with scrubby and sub-marginal land which would hardly support a crow. Suddenly four billion dollars' worth of oil is struck, eager under pressure of gas to burst into the light of day. "Ethics and ideals of the public weal go haywire under such pressure. Individualism turns rugged, ugly and reckless." For three years, 100,000 barrels of illegal oil a day have been pouring out of the field. Texas Rangers, enforcement officers, are powerless to check it. They are bribed, corrupted and occasionally murdered.

An owner spends $9,000 drilling a 3,600-foot well. He takes no risk, for the pool is there. He is legally permitted forty barrels a day, his tank to be regularly inspected. With oil at one dollar a barrel, this means $40 a day, $15,000 a year—a high return on his investment. But what is $15,000 when unlimited wealth lies there for the taking? So he taps his casing ten feet below the surface and runs a secret pipe out of it through which flow 1,000 barrels a day to bootleg trucks at fifty cents a barrel—$500 more a day, $180,000 a year! Or he puts a false bottom on his tank. Or he builds three false derricks above one well and secures an allowance of 160 barrels a day. Or he allows oil to leak into a stream and arranges with truckers to cart off the stream. Or he rigs faked valves.

Kilgore and Gladewater are roaring camps, centers of illegitimate refineries—lean-to, sheet-iron, tin-can, shack towns, with all the vices and meannesses, "blackened with the ugly but profitable slop of oil." Texans are individualists and their philosophy dulls the edge of enforcement. The courts are indulgent. The hot-oil gentry are not distinguished by thrift, hard work or foresight. They had the luck to get there first, and they possess considerable mechanical and political ingenuity. They happened to fall into a mine of black gold and they are cleaning up. Meanwhile the waste of oil and gas is prodigious beyond computation, and has demoralized the entire industry.*

Grainger County

In a few more years east Texas will be through, with most of its oil forever lost underground. This does not matter so much to the tin-can population, for they are used to moving on. What happens when the resource base is exhausted in a more settled community? Here for instance is Grainger County, Tennessee, as surveyed by Arthur L. Pollard. In a few cold figures he has presented the basic problem of America, reduced to negotiable proportions.

Grainger County is exclusively agricultural. Farmers have been on the soil for a hundred years. Nearly everything imported from outside its borders must be exchanged for soil or forest products within. There are no factories to be taxed or to provide employment; no railroads or power lines

* For confirmation of the above story, see an article by William A. Dupuy, in the *New York Times*, Jan. 27, 1935.

traverse the area; the people of the county possess no invested wealth in stocks or bonds. Their land and labor form
their only wealth. Nor do they own all their land, for many
are farm tenants and must pay outside owners. The county
consumes one-third of what it produces and sells two-thirds
to the world beyond. The county receives some alien revenue
from one large resort hotel, two inns and two gas stations.
There are 1,150 boys and girls from eighteen to twenty-
three years of age, of whom seven are in college. There are
900 passenger automobiles and 100 trucks. Residents who
have no cars have gone back to carts, and those who have
no carts, to sledges—for the trade of wheelwright has
disappeared. The average farm consists of seventy
acres—lot or waste. Such a farm can provide only bare
subsistence when worked by the owner under current
methods.

The average family is twenty per cent larger than the
average for the nation as a whole. At the age of twelve,
children begin leaving Grainger County for the world
outside. At age twenty-two the proportion of population is
less than that of the United States and it goes down steadily
until a low is reached at age thirty-three. Then it begins to
climb again, until at age fifty-three it levels the national
average. A whole world of tragic maladjustment lies in
these figures. The city, which has absorbed the youngsters,
begins to kick them out as middle age approaches. They
come drifting back, their youth and vigor gone, sacrificed
to no end except the steady depreciation of their homeland.

Here is Mr. Pollard's income account, somewhat con-
densed and rearranged:

GRAINGER COUNTY; ANNUAL LOSS AND GAIN ACCOUNT, 1932

Income:

Sales of crops		$425,000
Outside labor		20,000
Tourist income		20,000
Total operating income		465,000

Outgo:

Food purchased	155,000	
Clothing purchased	140,000	
Automobile expense	120,000	
Machinery, tools, fertilizer	40,000	
Education	10,000	
Miscellaneous expense	70,000	
Total operating outgo	535,000	
Interest paid	85,000	
Taxes—outside	20,000	
Miscellaneous losses	25,000	
Depreciation—buildings	80,000	
Depreciation—machinery	20,000	
Depletion—soil	55,000	
Total outgo		$820,000
Deficit of county		$355,000

How is this deficit met? It is not met, but is reduced in part by:

State aid for roads and schools	$ 60,000
Federal aid	51,000
Insurance receipts net	32,000
	$143,000

leaving a net deficit of $212,000.

The county thus keeps going by virtue of state and federal aid, by sinking more deeply into debt, by cumulative depreciation of its agricultural plant and by cumulative depletion of its natural resources. The end of the story cannot be long postponed. Grainger County can give up its motorcars, store clothes and farm machinery if it must, and live as its forefathers lived—with sledges, tallow candles and home-spun. It can get along without the world beyond if worst comes to worst. But two questions are in order: Can Detroit and International Harvester get along without Grainger County? Why did the native stock leave England and Scotland in 1700 only to achieve a standard of living in America in 1930 appreciably worse than that of the old country at the time they left?

A given community to function must either supply its own essentials, as in handicraft communities, or have some-thing to exchange for its essentials. Otherwise the com-munity has no economic underpinning and must either die or go on the dole. Grainger County, it appears, supplies less than one-third of its essentials at home and has a very serious shortage of goods and services to exchange for the remaining two-thirds. It is already on the state and federal dole, and is taking more out of the soil each year than it returns.

In modern times the choice of commodities to exchange offers considerable scope. New York City, in addition to its manufacturing activities, offers banking, brokerage and gambling services as well as night life and other sophistica-tions in return for the hearty support in tangible goods shipped in by the rest of the country. Atlantic City ex-changes sea air and bathing beauties. Florida exchanges sunshine and dog races; the county seat exchanges trading

238

facilities; Washington exchanges administration and the opinions of nine dignified gentlemen; Reno exchanges divorces; New England, which once exchanged textile manufacturing, turns to recreation; California exchanges vegetables, films and starry-eyed movements to regenerate mankind. All these "services," however, are based on tangible goods in the last analysis. The goods come first in any culture. Only when the stomach is assuaged can one turn to playing the market, to astrology or the fine arts. The tangible goods in turn are all based on natural resources.

Meanwhile it is true that in an abundance economy resources are comparatively flexible. For many standard resources substitutes are now available in whole or in part, and more may be expected as technology advances. It is also true that relatively few communities, strategically located and equipped with plenty of inanimate energy and a variety of automatic or semiautomatic factories and mechanized farms, could theoretically provide the bulk of all essentials for a much wider area. At a guess, under strict engineering control one-fourth of American communities, employing one-fourth of available labor, could furnish the necessities of life for the whole nation. This is the dream of the technocrats, and it is logical if not practicable.

For nearly two hundred years American communities functioned on the basis of self-support with exchange at a minimum. As the machine age developed after 1800, communities became increasingly specialized and exchange grew heavier. They specialized in raw materials, in fabrication of materials and later in services. This interdependence made for a larger per capita output and, on the whole, for higher living standards. Even Grainger County obtained its automobiles. But as community after community worked through its resources, the exchange balance went into the red.

Many communities, too, have lost their exchange balance by virtue of technological change, population shifts, transportation shifts, shifts in public demand. Consider the stranded coal towns, the shoe workers of Haverhill who have watched the industry drift west, the mill hands of Manchester and Lowell.

It is needless to labor the point. No American communities are today self-sufficient. Community A, which once had exchange values, has them no longer. Community B may have new values, but the people of A have come to call A home. They live on in their ghostly areas, loath to be torn up by the roots. Remember the letter from the woman in the Dust Bowl.

If some degree of conscious foresight is to be the order of the day, three alternatives present themselves:

1. Move people out of submarginal and blighted areas and replant them in communities which have a resource base or other exchange medium. This demands a drastic and a psychologically dangerous experiment in planned migration on a vast scale.

2. Let the people stay and maintain them on the dole, their only function being that of consumers. This is technologically possible—indeed, is being carried on to the tune of some millions of individual cases at the present time—but is fantastic from the human point of view. It means maintaining one-quarter of the nation, more or less, as a huge charitable asylum. A scholar of my acquaintance, Dr. Robert

240

Montgomery of the University of Texas, has offered a strictly logical plan. He proposes that we take a few million acres of the public domain, surround it with a heavy barbed-wire fence and armed guards and place therein the millions of Americans who have no resources and no jobs. Their only duty will be to consume. They will be enjoined to keep down the commercial surpluses of wheat, cotton, coal, oranges and motorcycles. Large appetites and destructive ability to wear out clothes will be encouraged. Meanwhile, the rest of the population will all have jobs, plenty of hard work and the satisfaction of knowing that the professional consumers will eat the economic system into profitable scarcity, that prices will remain safely high and that disastrous depressions will be prevented.

3. Reconstruct the resource base of those communities where reconstruction is possible. Where it is flatly impossible, planned migration will have to be resorted to. Reconstruction means building up the soil, restoring the forest and grass cover, checking erosion, reconditioning the fisheries, taming the rivers, encouraging wild life and recreation areas, supplying cheap energy, establishing a certain number of new local industries—but not enough to result in wasteful duplication, maintaining a large program of public works, particularly in the field of conservation, to provide local cash income. On these conditions, and only on these conditions, can the people of hundreds of American communities continue to call the homeland home.

Oust them, feed them or recondition them—so that they may presently feed themselves. The last makes more sense politically and psychologically than the other two. The

241

second makes more engineering sense, as efficiency is at a maximum, but psychologically and politically it is highly dubious.

This is what America faces today, and increasingly tomorrow. The New Deal as a whole has been fumbling around with all three policies. The Tennessee Valley Authority is planted solidly on the last proposition: Let the valley people stay in their homes and recondition the resource base. That is what makes it so important and so human.

Before examining the TVA and various other attempts at reconstruction and conservation, let us now, in the light of what has gone before, try to arrange the major principles of resource planning in orderly sequence. I have sought to show what has happened, and why it has happened. What is to be done about it? The next chapter will deal with some things that, in my opinion, ought to be done. The final chapters deal with what is actually being done.

Chapter XIV

PLANNING WITH NATURE

ECONOMIC planning may be roughly defined as an answer to the question: Where is the next meal coming from? It has been practiced by mankind for a good many thousands of years. If one lives on a tropical island with breadfruit and coconuts within easy reach, planning is at a minimum. In brisker latitudes not many full meals grow on trees. With the advent of civilization, the question was made collective and was usually addressed to a great river basin—the Nile, the Euphrates, the Yellow River—while the foresight ran to the next high water season and the next planting, sometimes to a whole series of future plantings. In modern times, not only food is involved but all the essentials of livelihood and even some of the luxuries.

Every human being is forced to make plans, but these do not concern us here. Our concern is rather with the community. How shall its base of natural resources be maintained? How shall its vitality be preserved? How shall its levels of living be raised? How shall it live more fully, and its children more fully still? Per contra, how shall a threatened menace to its livelihood be averted?

243

The Free Market

Under the traditional free-market system, the assumption is that human wants pull the strings, businessmen and bankers respond, capital flows in the required direction, labor is employed, prices find their own level, and automatically, without conscious direction, out come the goods and services. No community foresight is required; the system takes care of itself. The individual businessman, of course, is usually forced to plan his output in advance of his assured sales, but unless he has a monopoly such forward planning amounts to little more than shrewd guesswork. Every summer I sit down with the manager of a small publishing concern in New York and attempt to determine the number of copies we shall print of an annual trade publication. We look at the records for the last five years; we look at the state of this particular trade; we compare sales of similar publications this year and last. Then we take the plunge. Start the presses with a run of 45,000! The figure is nothing but a tempered guess. Sometimes we are 10,000 short and once we were 15,000 over—a sad time indeed.

The free market is a magnificent theory. For a century and a half the human mind has been enchanted with its logic and symmetry. Each man strives for his own gain, the gears whiz, and the product drops out. To devotees of this philosophy the mere mention of economic planning is both sacrilege and menace. Whoever touches the automatic gears risks losing his hand, if not indeed his immortal soul. The air is filled with bitter words—bureaucracy, regimentation, goosestep, blueprints, autocracy, tinkering with natural law.

244

But if we look under the words and the emotions they arouse to the real world, we find three facts. First, a large section of economic activity concerned with public business lies outside the free-market system, and here planning has been practised for generations. Second, within its own boundaries the system has been corrupted by monopolies, cartels, price-fixing agreements, trade associations, labor-union wage agreements, and, above all, by what Dr. Gardiner C. Means calls *administrative competition*. Third, the free-market system never made provision for a limited supply of national resources. Resources were to be exploited for a maximum of current income today, without thought of future income. This is well illustrated in the hot-oil fields of east Texas.

Monopolies and Administered Prices

Dr. Means presents figures to prove that the free market has lost well over half its membership through the arbitrary restrictions imposed by big business.* Sometimes these take the form of outright monopoly—like the Aluminum Company of America, sometimes trade-association agreements, sometimes a cartel, national or international, sometimes administrative competition, where a few great corporations, dominating an industry, find it less costly to restrict production than to lower prices when demand declines. About 200 corporations account for more than half of all industrial production. Little business, on the other hand, still in the free-market arena, invariably is forced to lower prices. When wheat and cotton fell to unheard-of depths in 1930, agri-

* Senate Document 13, 74th Congress.

culture actually increased its output in the effort to keep its gross income at par. Mr. Wallace, as we noted earlier, lifted American agriculture bodily out of the free-market system, thus giving it some of the advantages of big business. The Supreme Court threw it back to the lions.

American industry reveals the basic inconsistency between modern technology and the principles of the free market, between method and purpose. Under the impetus of its engineering achievements, it has given the world unprecedented techniques in organizing and planning industrial operations. It has developed admirable mechanisms for managerial control. Depending on the function to be performed, tools have been developed for the coordination and control of machines, sequences and labor. But the objective of this superb body of scientific management is chiefly pecuniary gain. One may say that American industry has planned insight, but no planned foresight. It plans on a functional basis for a nonfunctional objective.

The net result has been of course that, while American industrial techniques are the wonder of the world, American industrial depressions are an even greater wonder. For the first six years of the current depression the United States lost 100 billion man-hours of work through unemployment, and beggared itself of some 200 billion dollars' worth of goods and services which the industrial plant was equipped to produce.

The free market as an automatic regulating machine has stripped its gears. Products no longer fall out; they have to be dragged out. Those who continue to rely exclusively on this battered contraption to provide community livelihood are in the position of a man who selects a motorcar from a junk pile. The fact that it was a good car once will not give him much mileage. The free market still has its uses in certain areas, but it is too late to regard it as a substitute for planning.

Public Business

Foresight for certain phases of livelihood without regard to markets, prices and pecuniary demand has long been practised in the United States by the Army, the Navy, the public-school system, highway departments, municipal water supply, the Coast Guard, the Forest Service, public health, recreation and many other institutions. Zoning ordinances are common measures. A good part of the state of Wisconsin is zoned.

The essence of public business planning is to assess a need through the future and to take whatever steps are necessary to meet that need, regardless of immediate profit or loss. Such projects are normally undertaken, not because they "pay," but because the continuing vitality of the community is thought to demand them. Cost is, of course, a consideration, but other considerations involved are perhaps more important, such as security of life, prevention of epidemic disease or of starvation and want, continuance of vital services like transportation and national defense. The War Department has prepared an elaborate program for "M Day," the opening day of the next war. It comprehends the mobilizing of the whole population and a rigid control of resources, raw materials, manufacturing and transport. Free-market considerations will be thrust aside to the sole end of winning the war. This last is a form of planning against which business leaders make little audible protest.

A friend of mine executes school-building surveys for various towns and cities. She is an expert in the federal Bureau of Education. Her chief task is to extend population curves into the future. How many children between the ages of thirteen and nineteen will there be in the town of Mount Vernon in 1950? Upon the answer depends the program for the new high school. The American highway system is a vast integrated network jointly maintained by local, state and federal authorities. Here again population, traffic density and the rise in motor transport are the controlling factors. They are figured for years ahead, and the question of whether or not highways pay does not enter the long-range calculations.

In addition to public business of this direct nature, there is a large amount of what might be called *supervisory planning* in the regulation of certain utilities and industries. Examples are the various railroad controls of the Interstate Commerce Commission, now being extended to other forms of transport, the Public Utilities Commissions of several states, the Federal Power Commission, the Federal Trade Commission, the Federal Reserve System and many others. These controls, often covering rates, investment and other strategic matters, may be good, bad or indifferent, but at least they serve to remove the regulated industry from the free market. Regulation is the traditional American method of economic planning. It attempts to provide private business with conscious direction and foresight. It usually originates after the businessman's blind driving has taken him into a stone wall and the community is forced to install traffic signals. A recent example is the Securities Exchange Commission for the regulation of stock markets.

One would hesitate to estimate what percentage of all economic activity in the United States is now planned public business, of one type or another, but my guess would be at least one-third. The depression not only has greatly extended the area but has brought a strong demand for some kind of over-all coordination.

Natural Resources

The free-market system, even if it could be trusted automatically to throw off adequate amounts of food, clothing and shelter, does not allow and never has allowed for the conservation of capital in the form of natural resources. Case after case has been recited in the foregoing pages. The best conceivable way to waste a pool of petroleum is to parcel out the surface land to competing owners, each feverishly intent upon outdrilling his neighbors. Lumber companies are forced by competitive conditions to look upon a forest as a mine, and only the Forest Service, protecting future generations, can afford to look upon it as a crop. Mining companies must head for the richest veins when prices are dropping, whatever the consequent violation of sound engineering practice. Once I visited a silver mine in Mexico. Deep underground the various veins were painted according to the price of silver. Each morning radio brought the world price to the remote mountain valley, and each morning the crew filed into the mine to hew out the vein which the price dictated.

A more devastating practice from the engineering point of view is difficult to imagine.

The Geological Survey gives us an impressive table of the natural resources already held on federal government lands:

Thirty million acres of coal lands, containing more than 200 billion tons.

Five hundred thousand acres of phosphate lands, containing eight billion tons.

Large deposits of potash.

Sixty-five developed oil and gas fields, producing thirty-three million barrels a year.

Four million acres of shale, holding 60 billion barrels of oil.

Five million horsepower of developed hydroelectric power.

Eighteen million horsepower undeveloped.

Almost 200 million acres of public domain, containing much forest and range land.

One hundred million acres in which the government has parted with the surface title, but retains the subsurface or mineral title.

The only considerable deposit of helium in the world.

By the default of private enterprise, the task of conservation has passed and will continue to pass to the government. Private enterprise has had no plans save a maximum of pecuniary return. J. Russell Smith drives the conclusion home:

In Dayton, Ohio, in the age before regimentation, people laid off streets and lots and built houses on the low lands by the river's brim. In due time, the river rose and drowned them, after which the survivors subjected themselves to the Miami Conservancy

District. This new type of government was made to cope with floods. It levies taxes, it builds dams, it issues permits for struc-tures, thereby preventing people from building homes in places where they may be drowned. Thus regimented, present-day Daytonians are safe. The free Daytonians drowned.

Whatever verbal symbols we may cherish in our heads, modern communities in the power age have practised planning in respect to public business, have abandoned the free market and its automatic controls wherever big business is dominant and have had to accept the task of husbanding natural resources. It should also be pointed out that, despite lip service to a dying free market, Americans are becoming increasingly conscious that they possess the technical knowl-edge, the resources and the manpower to give a high standard of living to the last family. They have great faith in technical progress and the machine and in their ultimate ability to provide abundance and security.

Income and Capital Planning

During the depression the American communities, in common with nations all over the world, were obliged to make provisions for the gratuitous distribution of essentials —food, clothing, fuel—to a large fraction of the population. Private enterprise having failed to furnish necessities, the community was forced to do so at the pain of wholesale starvation or incipient revolution. Relief was given both in money and in kind. The plans were of the panic variety in most cases, unsuitable for permanent adoption. The several governments did what they could, with one eye on grumb-

251

ling bread lines and the other on long-established vested interests. The various New Deals, both here and abroad, might be termed *temporary planning for income*.

The problems with which this book has been concerned were accentuated by the depression but did not arise from it. The roots lay deeper. The waste of natural resources had already reached a point where planning and foresight for a permanent country were mandatory. Foresight in respect to resources is primarily planning for *capital*, in contrast with income planning described above.

In double-entry bookkeeping, every entry normally appears on both the capital account and the income account. The cashier credits sales and debits cash. Similarly, no clean distinction is possible between capital and income planning. Resources are maintained, not because they look impressive, but because people must eat—if not today, then tomorrow. We are confining our study primarily to resource or capital foresight, but it must never be forgotten that its only function in the long run is to furnish current supplies at some point in time.

If one is designing a vacuum-tube amplifier, says Mr. King Hubbert, the first question is to ask: What is it expected to do? And then: Over what range of frequencies is it to amplify? How many decibels' gain is it to have? What is to be its noise level? Then: What are the elements of design that will satisfy these performance specifications? Finally: What are the available materials? The designer is then ready to go ahead. Similarly we approach the social mechanism. An improved design is in order, and the specifications might read as follows:

The social mechanism is to produce the highest per capita standard of living, at the lowest man-hour cost, without stoppages or violent fluctuations and with a minimum wastage— or the highest efficiency of conversion—of natural resources.

Nature as Dictator

Resource planning involves a dictator. Gentlemen in club windows nod savagely. They see parades of bureaucrats, waving blueprints and, like Moses, laying down the laws of Thou Shalt and Thou Shalt Not. But they are wrong. The dictator is nature. In considering the Great Wheel of inter-related processes, we have discovered the terms on which she will keep a continent viable, healthy and permanent. The task of resource or capital planning is to meet those terms. The gentlemen in club windows say that planning subverts the "natural order," by which they mean the free market. This is an exceedingly superficial deduction. Laissez faire is a man-made institution, impermanent and passing. Nature has been here a long time. Her order, and hers alone, is *natural*.

If constitutions, statutes, laws of property, boundary lines and individual rights and duties require readjustment, nature provides the bench mark. Fortunately she is flexible, and not much given to blueprints. The first job of any agency proposing to cooperate with her, however, is to map the region over which planning is proposed, showing such relevant facts as topography, slope, soils, rainfall and stream flow. Only thus may the planners learn nature's terms.

The shift from animate to inanimate energy has remade the resource map of the world. Zimmerman calls it "the Great

Divide." There is nothing comparable in history. People once "raised food and feed today to generate the energy required to raise food and feed tomorrow." The net surplus was small or nonexistent. But with energy derived from coal, oil and falling water, man can control metabolism to a certain extent. Energy from food and feed is subject to the law of diminishing returns; the utilization of coal and oil can be consciously improved. It is this new power which gives us margin to support 130 million people, and support them well. Sheer area of land as the basis of food supply is less important than it was before the Great Divide. But land is still *situs*, a place to live. Soil depletion can conceivably be compensated for by growing food in tanks, but not the collateral effects of flood, pollution, water shortage, siltage and destruction of *situs*. The people of Ducktown cannot live by copper alone. The Great Wheel turns, and, if we gamble on fuels and metals as our sole support, the stakes will go the way of Radio, common, in 1929.

THE RESOURCE HIERARCHY

The balance of nature and modern technology in its use of fuels and metals are locked together, and together they support the American population. If technology goes out, population is cut in half; if the balance of nature goes out, population disappears. The principles of resource planning on the highest level of abstraction are two:

Hold soil, water, forest and grass at par. Over any reasonable period of time never allow net depletion. Keep inflow balanced against outflow.

254

Hold the rate of mineral exploitation at a minimum, except for abundant resources like stone and sand. Prevent needless waste. Encourage vigorous research in the field of substituting abundant minerals for rare ones

On these two principles, the resource base remains solid to perpetuity in respect to land and water and declines at a minimum rate in respect to minerals. Land and water we might term the *active* resources, minerals the *passive*. Trees grow, water runs, the hydrologic cycle revolves on its majestic wheel. Minerals lie dormant in their beds, and grow only in geologic time.

The time elements in replacement should also be kept in mind. They run something like this:

1. *Grass.*—This is the resource which can be replaced most quickly, sometimes within a year, but in the Dust Bowl not for many years.

2. *Forest.*—It can be replaced in from 20 to 200 years, depending on the species of trees planted.

3. *Waters.*—Artesian basins may sometimes be refilled in a few years if pumping is stopped, but most basins, lakes, rivers and ponds, when they have run low or dry, wait for their replacement on the forest cycle.

4. *Soils.*—Replacement by natural means requires centuries to thousands of years.

5. *Metals.*—Once mined they can never be replaced, but by remelting scrap metal their useful life can be prolonged.

6. *Fuels.*—Coal, oil, gas, peat. Once used they are gone forever as men measure time. Geologic processes might conceivably replace them.

7. *Wild Life.*—An extinct animal, like the passenger pigeon, can never be replaced by either geology or biology.

River-basin Principles

A river basin cannot be planned for any one factor, like navigation alone, or flood control alone—unless we descend to random tinkering. Look at the failure of the flood controllers in the lower Mississippi, with river and levees rising like an elevated railroad across the plain. If floods are to be tamed, one must go back to where the water starts, at the raindrop and rill stage. Marsh, swamp, grass, forest, artesian basin, type of crop—all must come in. We might call this *headwater strategy*, playing the game with nature rather than playing against her with levees. The individual farmer is very important in headwater strategy; his cooperation is essential. From raindrop to river mouth, two principles are paramount: Hold the water! Release it slowly, using every gallon as it comes down. Wherever possible, hold water in the soil and natural reservoirs rather than by costly dams. Categorically, watershed and river principles include:

Flood waters held at a minimum.
Dry season flow at a maximum.
Forest on the steep slopes.
Grass on the less rugged slopes.
Control of erosion on all crop lands.
Rigorous control of pollution by human and industrial wastes.
Safeguarding of domestic water supplies.
Preservation of fish and game.
Maintenance of the levels of artesian basins.
Engineering of irrigation and drainage projects in line with water conservation.
Maintenance of marsh and swamp lands as reservoirs.

256

PLATE XI.—PROTECTED VALLEY. (*Mississippi Valley Committee.*)

Supplementary irrigation on the farm.

The wide use of surplus hydroelectric power derived from the above projects.

"A river is more than an amenity; it is a treasure." Treat it as such. Do not befoul its banks with dumps and shacks and untreated sewage outlets. Each basin must be studied to determine precedence of uses and means of coordination. The Supreme Court has ruled that drinking water for man is the highest use. Abstractly it is; in concrete cases, it may not be. In the Colorado basin, engineers would place irrigation, power, flood control and perhaps recreation ahead of potable water. It depends on the river.

Planning from the purely economic point of view is a difficult task. New invention is continually upsetting nice calculations. Public demand is fickle and may turn from products carefully planned for. Industrial migrations, population changes, new forms of transport, prefabricated houses, confuse the issue. Suppose we had planned in detail for a horse-and-buggy economy, and then along came the automobile! I am a strong proponent of industrial planning provided it is kept flexible, but I realize its difficulties. How different the case may be when one turns to planning for a river basin. Here nature sets the terms. The scattered pieces of the puzzle all fit together. The hydrologic cycle operates yesterday, today and forever. When the concept of land and water as an organic whole is driven home, one finds firm ground under one's feet. This area demands forests, that grass; water must be held on another. Arguments fall to a minimum. Only fools and speculators grow disputatious. Economic landmarks are constantly shifting. Watersheds stay put.

In spite of some duplication of what has gone before, it will be well to summarize the general principles which should guide land planning. The duplication occurs because land and water can be separated in the dictionary but not in fact.

Forest Principles

A permanent yield of raw timber; annual cut not to exceed annual growth—for the nation as a whole if not for a given region.·

Forest management to preserve soils against erosion, to halt forest fires, to keep water supplies pure, to keep floods at a minimum, to hold levels of artesian basins, to maintain wild life and fisheries, to promote recreation.

The extensive use of tree crops—nuts, persimmons, mulberries, etc.—as food for man and beast. Thus tree crops replace tilled crops in special circumstances.

The use of substitute materials for building—cement, stone, clay, glass, composition board—when permanent lumber yield is threatened.

Grass Principles

A permanent yield of pasture for animal food; strict regulation against overgrazing.

Increase in production of foods derived from grass rather than from tilled crop, especially more milk, of which the nation has a shortage; less cereals, of which there is a surplus.

Grass management, similar to forest management, to preserve soils against erosion—both wind and water—to safeguard water supplies and to control floods.

Crop-land Principles

The preservation of the physical soil against erosion by terracing, strip planting, contour plowing, crop rotation, gully planting and check dams. No plowing on slopes of more than ten to twelve per cent.

Putting as much mineral matter back into the soil as crops take out.

Supplementary irrigation.

Wild-life Principles

Restrict pollution, silting and excess salt at river mouths.

Provide more refuges, sanctuaries, migratory-bird treaties, breeding grounds, wilderness areas.

Restrict "gatling-gun" hunting and fishing, both by commercial interests and by sadists.

Educate sportsmen.

The above principles will maintain the active base of land and water. If they are followed, the terms of nature will be met. A region or a continent will no longer go downhill. At the same time, with careful management, the current output in food and technical crops, like cotton, lumber, tree crops and water power, is in no danger of restriction in the long run. On the contrary, it should steadily increase. In the United States, if annual timber cut were held to annual growth by sudden fiat, a shortage would indeed result. We can hardly get on a permanent-yield basis before 1950 (see Chapter VIII). The principle of permanent yield is sound enough, but the introduction must be gradual, accompanied by a great program of reforestation in cut-over areas and on lands now in crops which should go back to forest.

Industry is based on diminishing assets, and thus is impermanent. Some day the metals will be gone. Land and water go on forever, if we care to work with nature. Their values need never decline. They are the only final insurance of the life of our country and its people.

Mineral Principles

The planning problem here is to protect a diminishing store.

Use substitutes from the active base for mineral fuels wherever possible. Plant fuels like wood are not practicable in most cases, but water power can frequently be substituted for coal or oil. Use coal in preference to oil as a fuel; there is more of it left. If watershed principles are in operation, only the next ice age will exhaust hydroelectric power.

Save metals by a maximum use of scrap. Thus iron, copper, lead and zinc can be used over and over again. This principle has long been highly regarded in Europe and is beginning to penetrate the consciousness of America. Do not use metals for purposes which permanently destroy them—as lead and zinc for paint—if it can be avoided. Do not expose them to corrosion, which also limits a return to scrap.

Reduce waste in the mining, refining and utilization of minerals. This is an old story but its importance cannot be too frequently emphasized. Devote minerals to those uses for which they possess peculiar qualifications. Petroleum, which is peculiarly adapted for lubricating oil and transport fuel, should not be used to raise steam in factory boilers.

Substitute abundant minerals for rare ones wherever possible. Encourage research to promote the use of aluminum, cement, clay, sand, stone, gravel, shale and other materials which are plentiful in the earth's crust. Aluminum can replace copper in many uses, saving copper for those things which it alone can perform.

"The real heart of conservation," says L. C. Gray, "is the conflict between the present and the future. . . . The primary problem, expressed in economic language, is the determination of the proper rate of discount on the future with respect to utilization of natural resources." The principles enumerated above will not save minerals from an ultimate exhaustion. There is no way of coming to terms with nature in the matter of passive deposits—unless and until man devises a method of fashioning raw materials from atomic bricks. We can, however, lower the rate of exhaustion to a point where the technology of substitutes offsets the decline. At such a point the community may cease to worry about its minerals.

How different is the approach to the active assets. While the injunction is to use rare metals less (modern war, of course, is the greatest destroyer of metals conceivable), water should be used more: Make it work all the way down; use it over and over again. The Tennessee Valley Authority is putting water to work in the first comprehensive program of planning with nature ever attempted in America. Let us examine it.

Chapter XV

TENNESSEE VALLEY

IN WASHINGTON you find acres of office work set in a stately remote city. The nation is being saved by a hurricane of interoffice memoranda going round and round. The saviors wear a slightly confused air. One supposes that the spiral whirls upward, but one is not always sure. So many Corinthian columns, so many filing cases, so many sheets of paper, with twice as many carbons.

You climb into a car and drive west from Washington, over the red fields of Virginia, up the Blue Ridge Mountains, down the Shenandoah Valley, with billboards screaming of limestone caves, up the Appalachians again, with the Great Smokies looming to the south, and down into Tennessee and the valley of the Tennessee, running yellow with silt. You come to Knoxville, and hard by it the town of Norris and the Norris Dam. Here are filing cases and interoffice memoranda too, but towering above them is the dam itself, solid and eternal as the temples of Karnak. Its lofty, concrete face is the reality of achievement behind the paper work. Those who strive to help the valley are not confused. They do not seem to move in circles and spirals; they move, like the profile of their dam, in straight lines. One feels their excitement. It is a very revealing experience to go from Washington to Knoxville. It might be a good idea for the Secretary of the Interior to build a thundering big dam on the Potomac.

The story runs that one of the TVA staff went north to Ontario to see how the Hydro was functioning. He stopped a farmer on the road and asked him what, after twenty years of experience, he thought of the government power system.

"I think it's a fine thing."

"Why?"

"Well, stranger, there are a lot of reasons, but the biggest reason is that it keeps the young folks at home. The smartest ones used to go off to the cities, and now most of them stay on the farms. There is so much right here to interest them."

As we shall see, cheap electric power is not the only function of the TVA, probably not even the most important function in the long run. The Ontario farmer, however, stated the ultimate goal as well as it can be stated in a phrase. The TVA is an attempt to keep a region viable, healthy and interesting and to hold the oncoming generations on their homeland. In Grainger County the young folks went off to the city, to return beaten in their later years.

One day, with Benton MacKaye and the foresters, I climbed far up on the shoulder of Le Conte, one of the giants of the Great Smokies. Looking west, we saw the great valley unroll before us until it was lost in the mists of the horizon—fields, woodlots, meadow lands, villages, the sparkle of rivers and the mountain wall around. Fields run high on the mountain slopes. Years ago farmers used to supplement their income by day labor in mines and forests. Such work has largely disappeared. The cornfields grew steeper, increasing the erosion rate, promoting floods and silting the streams and rivers.

The peak on which we stood, the splendid forest of hemlock, beech, poplar and rhododendron through which we had climbed, the tumbled crags to the north, east and south, were the property of the United States government. A good part of the mountain wall, from which the little waters fall to make the tributaries which in turn make the Tennessee River, is national forest or national park. Nearly five million acres, more than one-quarter of all the forest land in the valley, is government owned. The TVA is thus not an isolated experiment, but is yoked with large projects in silviculture and recreation which preceded it. Headwater strategy may be practised under the best of circumstances.

These waters come down from Virginia, North Carolina, Georgia, and eastern Tennessee in a series of rivers which meet not far from Knoxville to form the main river. This region is tumultuous at the height of land, rugged below with steep cornfields and little farms tucked into the mountain "coves," then rolling land with broader farms and finally, in the cottonfields of Alabama, almost flat. The elevation descends from 6,000 to 250 feet, giving a climate which ranges from that of the Great Lakes to subtropical. The rainfall is heavy, varying from 50 to 80 inches. The valley can grow anything which now grows between Canada and the Gulf. It is the perfect laboratory for an experiment in regional planning.

264

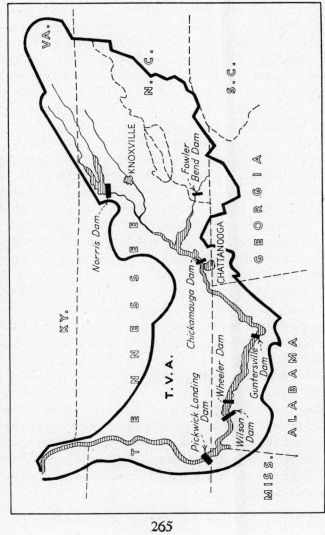

MAP 9.—TENNESSEE RIVER BASIN

The basin is shaped like a butterfly with the narrow waist at Chattanooga. The east wing is larger and more rugged, swelling over the eastern part of Tennessee and clipping off segments of Virginia, North Carolina and Georgia. Here is where the water comes from; this is the region of heaviest rainfall. The Powell and Clinch rivers join at Norris Dam to pour into the Tennessee some eighty miles below. The west wing is the course of these united waters from Chattanooga down into Alabama, over Muscle Shoals— where the Wilson Dam was built during the war, and which formed the nucleus of the TVA—across the corner of Mississippi, then due north through western Tennessee into Kentucky and finally into the Ohio River at Paducah, not far from where the Ohio pours into the Mississippi at Cairo.

The Tennessee contributes about twenty per cent of the flood waters of the Mississippi. The valley is an entity, true, but at its mouth it locks into the water economy of the whole Mississippi basin. It is the fourth largest river in America, but extremely temperamental. Its flow varies from 8,000 to 500,000 cubic feet per second. Flood damage has been terrific. The average loss at Chattanooga is $700,000 a year.

The valley cuts across seven states and contains some 40,000 square miles of territory, about four-fifths the area of England. It has a population of nearly two and one-half million people, only a quarter of whom live in cities. More than half the region is forested, but hardly virgin. Nearly all has been cut over, and much of it burned and depleted in accordance with traditional practice. There are coal, iron, copper, phosphate and other minerals in the valley, and millions of horsepower in the rush of the rivers. There are a number of factories, but the region as a whole is not industrial. It has lived, or tried to live, primarily on its raw resources—forest, pasture, soil, minerals.

The average annual cash income of the 4,000 families moved from the Norris reservoir site was under $100. This failed signally to provide the relatively simple wants of the group. Wants have been studied with some care and include:

20 acres of crop land	Plenty of children
A tight five-room house	Some old-fashioned religion
1 horse	1 radio
1 cow	1 automobile
1 hog	1 washing machine
Chickens	Access to the movies

A reasonable chance for a little neighborly litigation.

This, you will admit, is not an exorbitant budget—save possibly on the score of children—but $100 per family, plus the self-subsistence labor of the family, falls far short of it. The people of the upper valley are hospitable, proud, salty, independent, illiterate by modern standards and desperately poor. They are poor because many of their ancient crafts have lapsed or because in the highly specialized economy of today the exchange value of these crafts is low. Grainger County, whose resource base we examined in Chapter XIII, lies in the valley, and part of it will be under water when the Norris reservoir fills. It is typical of many districts.

The TVA is a special kind of corporation without capital stock The federal government controls it and Congress

267

votes its appropriations. In addition, it receives considerable income from the sale of power, and in the future will receive more. It will probably never be self-supporting in the strict financial sense, for it is public business—like schools and highways—beyond the rigid bookkeeping of private enterprise. It is now operated (1936) by three directors: Dr. Arthur E. Morgan, college president and dam builder extraordinary; Dr. H. A. Morgan, specialist in soils and phosphates, former president of the University of Tennessee, the man who drove the cattle tick below the Rio Grande; and David C. Lilienthal, sometime Public Service Commissioner of Wisconsin. Dr. Arthur E. Morgan is chairman, builds the dams and develops labor policy. Dr. H. A. Morgan builds good will among the people of the valley and develops soil control. Mr. Lilienthal attends to power and the strenuous assaults of the power trust. Fortunately, he likes to fight. The National Resources Board believes that five directors plus a general manager would provide a better executive machine, but no one doubts that President Roosevelt has chosen three outstanding individuals. The authority is both a planning and an administrative agency. It has a large planning division and an even larger executive force. Most planning groups in America have no administrative function; they just advise.

The Constitution of the United States knows nothing of regional planning, for the conception would have been fantastic in 1787, when a specialized exchange economy was still unborn. The Supreme Court knows nothing of regional planning except in the negative sense that a river basin comprising portions of seven states is suspect in the light of the commerce clause, and probably unlawful. Congress has never heard of regional planning officially, and would be seriously confused as to the patronage involved if it had. The President had a definite idea as to the functions and scope of the TVA. He saw the river basin as a geographic and hydrologic unit. He wanted to make the people therein more comfortable, and he wanted to set up a series of yardsticks to measure power facilities, rural electrification, flood control, erosion control and progressive agriculture —yardsticks to be applied in other regions in the hope of making people more comfortable there. Many members of Congress undoubtedly shared these desires with the President, especially Senator Norris, who has been the tireless and devoted guardian of Muscle Shoals for a decade.

Under the American political system one cannot go straight to one's desire. One must adopt a crablike course which defers to established taboos and symbols. To control the Tennessee in the interests of the people living within the valley is legally outrageous, as Professor Arnold of the Yale Law School ironically suggests, and not to be tolerated by right-thinking citizens. But both navigation and flood control have slid past the taboos in times gone by and are now admitted as right and necessary functions. Federal production and sale of power, however, were on the fence until the United States Supreme Court settled the question in the affirmative by eight votes to one, early in 1936.

The TVA act was framed with these taboos in mind. It provides for:

1. A maximum development of the Tennessee River for navigation.

269

2. A maximum amount of flood control.

3. A maximum generation of electric power consistent with flood and navigation control.

4. The investigation of a proper use of marginal lands.

5. Studies on reforestation.

6. Recommendations for "the economic and social well-being of the people living in said river basin."

This last provision was perhaps too frank. It may yet prove the undoing of the whole experiment. It comes perilously close to stating what the act was really designed for. It is bad form and bad law to consider the social well-being of two million people scattered over seven states. Such frankness was not really necessary. All that needed to be stipulated was navigation, and nature would do the rest, even including the welfare clause. Why? Because you cannot construct a nine-foot navigation channel from Paducah to Knoxville without tinkering with the whole flow of water down the basin, which involves the hydrologic cycle, which dominates and controls the ecology of the region, and which thus admits the whole program— animal, vegetable and human. Of course, you can dig a nine-foot channel at fabulous expense without considering any of the related factors, but the first spring flood will damage it and silt rushing down from the eroded fields will complete the ruin. Various "navigable" channels have been so constructed in the past, but they have fallen under the general title of the congressional pork barrel. There is no pork to be had in the TVA, as any member of Congress will sadly tell you, but instead a strict interpretation of a permanent nine-foot channel.

270

When you put a nine-foot channel up to nature and ask that it be made permanent, what does she stipulate? She first makes it clear that what goes up must come down. The people of Hartford, the people of Pittsburgh, the people of Johnstown have no illusions on this score. Dependable navigation calls for flood control; flood control calls for dams and reservoirs; reservoirs must not fill with silt or their function vanishes. Hales Bar Dam in the big river has become thirty-three per cent silted in twenty-three years. Silt, as we have seen, can be prevented only by the control of erosion on agricultural lands and little waters. Erosion control calls for cover crops, both forest and grass, and scientific methods in tillage and crop rotation. Cover crops call for cheap fertilizer, otherwise they will not take root on the exhausted soils. Cheap fertilizer, especially phosphate, which is the major requirement in the valley, can best be made with the help of electric furnaces and cheap power. So the cycle completes itself, a house-that-Jack-built. If you really mean navigation, all these things will be added. Similarly, if the national taboos frowned on navigation and smiled on fertilizer, let us say, the cycle would be almost identical.

Nor does it stop here. Large reservoirs demand the removal of many houses, which calls for an intelligent resettlement program. They demand an extensive replanning of railways, highways, schools and recreation areas. The forest cover which is to check erosion calls for permanent management and many jobs for fire patrollers and forest workers. Large reservoirs often produce trillions of mosquitoes and in these latitudes mosquitoes spread malaria.

271

Malaria calls for a medical-engineering control as rigorous as the methods of Colonel Gorgas when the Panama Canal was built. Malaria is less lethal than yellow fever, but it is at least as hard to eradicate. Water control ties in with fish and wild-life preservation, with purification of streams polluted by city sewers and industrial wastes.

Such are nature's demands. In writing them down, I have also listed the functions of the TVA. To the list may be added certain collateral functions which appear to fit the cycle logically enough: a labor program for the very extensive engineering operations involved, primarily dams and reservoirs; the conservation of the valley's mineral resources, especially phosphate rock; the development of the hydroelectric power resources of the valley as one integrated low-cost system; the discovery of ways and means to put the power to useful employment, such as rural electrification. Other functions include land classification, aerial mapping, a program for the use of marginal lands and the development of domestic industries to supplement agriculture and provide employment.

We start with navigation and end with a comprehensive program of regional planning. As a matter of fact—and I trust the Supreme Court is safely asleep as I whisper it— navigation is probably the least important aspect of the cycle, from the point of view of the well-being of the people of the valley. Army engineers anticipate a very substantial traffic by 1950—some eighteen million tons, in fact—but it is safe to say that they have not anticipated all the technological developments which may occur in transport within the next fifteen years.

Dams

As one drives down the Tennessee Valley, its appearance is probably not much changed from ten years ago. This experiment which so agitates the nation is rather hard to find, unless one knows where to look. Ten years ago there was a great dam at Muscle Shoals, now called the Wilson Dam. It was equipped with generators for producing power and with two nitrate plants. These assets the TVA took over. The generators were put to work and power was sold to various private companies and to a few towns. One of the nitrate plants was converted into a laboratory for experiments on a cheap phosphate fertilizer. Headquarters were established in Knoxville, three hundred miles from the original property, and work was begun on a dam in the Clinch River, a tributary of the Tennessee, twenty-five miles from Knoxville. To house the dam workers and part of the headquarters' staff, the model town of Norris was built. The Norris Dam is now completed, generators are being installed, and power will flow in 1936. As the reservoir fills behind the dam, it will back upstream at least forty miles, and then the TVA will begin to make a very tangible impression on the landscape.

As skilled workers finish at Norris, they go to work on the Wheeler Dam, some twenty miles above the Wilson Dam. Wheeler is almost finished, and presently its reservoir will fill. A dam at Pickwick Landing is well under way. Construction has been started on dams at Guntersville and Chickamauga. When their reservoirs are full, the valley will have taken on a very different appearance indeed. Nor is this all. Dams are recommended for construction at

Gilbertsville, Watts Bar and Coulter Shoals on the main river, and two more tributary storage dams, like Norris, are proposed at Fontana and Fowler Bend.

There will be nine dams in the main river, including Hales Bar, built and leased by a private power company, and three in tributary rivers. With these twelve dams in place, the nine-foot channel running 650 miles from Knoxville to Paducah is assured and protected; no conceivable flood can seriously damage the valley, for the plans are based on a flow of water fifty per cent greater than the historic flood of 1867. The power load will be integrated from dam to dam, so that the resources of those where the water is low will be supplemented by those where the water is high. Any power engineer can tell you what this means in dependability and low cost. Great transmission lines will link generator to generator. To take a specific instance: Wilson Dam is a run-of-the-river plant. Its reservoir does not provide much storage, and in the summer and fall, when the river is normally low, its power output is at a minimum. Norris Dam, on the other hand, is designed primarily for storing flood waters and has a huge capacity. While Wilson is well supplied by the high river in the spring, the Norris gates will be closed; flood waters will fill the great reservoir. As Wilson declines, Norris comes in. The gates are opened. Power is generated once at the Norris turbines and, as the released water goes down the river, again at Wilson. Norris and Wilson together can generate three or four times as much dependable power as either could produce alone.

With nine run-of-the-river dams, it is conceivable that every bucket of water released from Norris or other tribu-

PLATE XII.—Generator tunnel, Norris Dam. (*Photo by Charles Krutch.*)

tary reservoir will be used ten times. By the summer of 1937, every bucketful will be used three times—once at Norris, once at Wheeler, once at Wilson. This is the engineering ideal of balancing the load, and it makes for cheap power. No private company can hope to rival such comprehensive engineering.

To the close of 1936, about $85,000,000 will have been spent on six dams—Wheeler, Norris, Pickwick Landing, Guntersville, Chickamauga and Fowler Bend. By the end of 1940 all six will be completed, Congress permitting, at a total cost of about $185,000,000. By 1944 another $144,-000,000 can be expended to advantage in constructing four more dams to make the system complete—Gilbertsville, Watts Bar, Coulter Shoals and Fontana. The total outlay is thus estimated at about a third of a billion—say the cost of a half-dozen battleships. The work has been planned to keep the skilled labor force steadily employed for the next eight years and preserve the human as well as the hydrologic balance. Labor costs under such a long-swing program will be at a minimum, as any personnel manager can tell you.

All the dams will have locks for navigation where necessary. All will have penstocks for power, but generators will not be installed until demand warrants it. Wilson, Wheeler and Norris are about to produce 205,000 kilowatts of continuous power. If and when the whole group comes in, the total will be raised to 660,000 kilowatts of continuous, dependable, year-round power.

Crop Lands

So much for dams, the bony skeleton of the TVA. Now for the flesh and blood. Looking around the valley, if your

275

eyes are sharp, you will find the face of nature on the farms being slowly changed. Twenty enterprising farmers in each county are allowing experiments in the control of erosion to be made on their farms. Steep slopes are going out of corn and cotton and back to grass or forest. Moderate slopes are being terraced or contour plowed. CCC boys are helping to plug gullies with little dams and thickets of black locust. Dr. H. A. Morgan's phosphates are bringing up green new grasses, presently to be grazed by livestock. A scientific plan of crop rotation is being followed.

Neighbors come and lean over the fences—first to scoff, then to be interested, finally to consider seriously a similar plan on their own farms. Already the farmers of the whole valley are interested. "Hit used to run off," said one highland farmer. "Now hit walks off!" Thus methods of agriculture primarily designed to keep reservoirs from filling with silt are causing one-crop farming to give way to diversified farming—a bitter need of the south. Farm diet is being improved and balanced with milk and vegetables. A way is being prepared to replace King Cotton, who is toppling from his throne. Twenty experimental farms in a county are not many. But the leaven spreads. If it continues to spread, the appearance of the valley will be changed in another way: pine on the steep hills where corn now grows, grass below. The cheap power may encourage electric pumps with little reservoirs and supplementary irrigation. The great red gashes of gully erosion will heal. Ten years from now, if all goes well, the valley will be a different place.

The total staff of the TVA now (1936) includes some 13,000 persons. About 5,000 are building engineering works;

4,000 are clearing reservoirs, most of them local farmers, unskilled in mechanical trades; upward of 4,000 are salaried workers, technical or clerical. Here we find engineers, foresters, experts in the control of erosion, ecologists, geologists, physicists, chemists, agronomists, medical and sanitation experts, architects, statisticians, economists, sociologists and educational experts. We find a young woman whose duty it is to pacify the few rugged individualists who announce noisily that they would rather drown beneath the rising reservoir than leave their cabins. The Liberty League should erect a monument to them, for they are as courageous as they are cracked. This young woman has a talent for absorbing their protestations and ultimately bringing them around.

The technical staff is not large considering the area involved—almost as large as England—and the mammoth task of reestablishing the economy of a whole region. This staff, however, is only the front line. Behind it is a more numerous army made up of local organizations: county agents, extension-service teachers from the land-grant colleges, school boards, farmers' cooperatives, the Red Cross, highway authorities and the staffs of other federal agencies— the Forest Service, the triple A, the triple C, the Resettlement Administration, the Bureau of Mines, the Reclamation Service (the greatest dam designers in the world, with Boulder Dam to prove it), the Geological Survey, the War Department, Army engineers and so on. The cooperation is genuine. There seems to be something about the boldness and vigor of the whole enterprise which fires the imagination and enlists enthusiastic support.

277

Norris Forest

Let me give you a concrete example of the TVA's projects. To protect the shores of Norris Reservoir from silting, pollution, mosquitoes and real estate operators, a quarter-mile strip surrounding the 775 miles of shore line has been purchased, a total of 117,000 acres. It is to be known as Norris Forest. People who have their farms in this area must be provided for. This demands a removal section in cooperation with the Resettlement Administration and the extension service of the University of Tennessee. Then airplanes must go aloft and take mosaic photographs of the whole region for a basic land-use map, to be checked by field surveys. The 117,000 acres will be divided into ten functional areas, and for each area expert technical study and planning are required.

1. Settlement areas, where farms will be continued, the farmers to receive dependable cash income from forest work.

2. Crop lands, where agriculture is advisable under proper tillage methods.

3. Grazing lands, for lease under strict control.

4. A permanent-yield forest of 76,000 acres. The lumber will produce revenue.

5. A tree-nursery area, including experimental work on vegetation which checks erosion and on forest crops which feed men and animals—black walnuts, Japanese chestnuts, persimmons, mulberries, pecans and many others. Incidentally, this is one of the most interesting experiments in the valley.

6. Game areas for restricted hunting, for protected breeding of wild fowl and for a sanctuary where no trespassing is permitted.

7. A wilderness area for solitude. No improvements of any kind to be permitted. Thoreau would find peace here.

8. A primeval area, where the remnants of the virgin forest are to be protected.

9. A study area (6,000 acres) as laboratory for ecologists. No hunting permitted.

10. Recreation areas for campers, hikers, boy scouts, leased camp sites and the rest. No hot dog stands.

All this is but one part of one reservoir. When airplanes are foolproof and cheap, I think I shall apply for a summer camp on the shores of Lake Norris. I know that its great natural beauty can never be spoiled under this program, but only enhanced. I shall enjoy driving on the Norris Freeway, a twenty-five-mile stretch of superb highway, its banks forever protected against billboards and other excreta. The freeway begins at the extensive tree nursery *below* the dam. A reporter from a prominent reactionary paper wrote a story after a flying trip to the TVA, pointing out that all this was typical of government inefficiency. Presently the reservoir would rise and flood the expensive nurseries and the freeway. His only trouble was that he could not tell upstream from down.

The Middle-road Technique

What vested interests are fighting the TVA? There is little organized opposition in the valley. New York, pulling the strings to its puppets in Tennessee, registers the very considerable opposition of the power companies and of certain bankers and businessmen. But the mass of the people are for it—farmers, workers, mechanics. Main street is for it. Professional and middle-class people generally are for it. Some politicians are disgruntled because their wards find no jobs at the TVA without first undergoing an exhaustive test by the personnel division as to technical competence. Nothing is more discouraging to a politician's second cousin. The Chattanooga Chamber of Commerce blows hot and cold. At a recent meeting two resolutions were passed, one deploring the TVA on high moral grounds as a violator of sound American institutions and the other demanding that all contracts for TVA supplies be let to Chattanooga businessmen. Thus the chamber roundly denounced the devil and in the same breath solicited his sulphur and brimstone business.

By and large, the valley has been won over. When the Supreme Court's affirmative decision was handed down, people burst into spontaneous parades and celebrations. This is due in part to the substantial cash disbursements which mighty engineering works entail. In greater part it is due to a friendly and diplomatic attitude. All three directors share this attitude, and all are responsible for it, but the initial credit probably goes to Dr. H. A. Morgan, because he has lived in the valley for forty years, studying its soil and learning to understand its people.

The TVA did not appear over the mountains, an alien swarm of bureaucrats, flourishing blueprints, prepared to tell the people of the valley what to do—and like it. The temper of the authority has been to ask the people: What do you want? How can we help you get it? This is your valley; you live in it. Perhaps we can show you some ways of doing things whereby you can live better. We shall be glad to try. And the residents, after the inevitable period of shock at anything new, were disarmed by this frankness. This basic

280

assumption that the people of the valley come *first* touched every member of the staff with whom I talked. All are interested in the men and women about them, especially the hill people with their strong characters and original points of view. Stories run in relays from office to office and from mouth to mouth. For instance:

TVA Census Taker: Have you any children?
Old Farmer: No, stranger, but I've got a dam fine hog.

TVA Erosion Man: Perhaps we can show you a little something about scientific agriculture.
Georgia Cracker: Well, sir, I've run through three farms, and pretty well used up this one. You can't tell me nothing about farming.

One Old Timer to Another: I tell you this TVA juice is cleaner than private company juice. It's made with running water and not with dirty coal.

Whenever possible, the TVA works through local groups which are already organized and functioning. If none exist, the TVA starts them. To obtain rural electric-power lines, farmers must first form a local cooperative. When approached, a given county may be on the defensive. So the TVA agents call a meeting and simply tell the story of what rural electrification means, what it costs and what its benefits are. Then they pack their charts and prepare to leave, remarking as they take their hats that this particular county is a difficult one to service. The meeting, they point out, was called to get the general news before the farmers. Some day, perhaps,

281

if all goes well, a line might be arranged, but hardly now. From defensive the audience turns to offensive. Why not now? What's the matter with this county? Why can't we have what other counties have? Mister, where are those blanks? We'll have a full list of names for you tomorrow, no, tonight, and we'll sign up that 662 kilowatts per mile. What do you mean, we can't have TVA power now? And the cooperative is enthusiastically launched under its own steam, with full local responsibility.

The TVA Act directs that surplus power shall be sold first to public groups—cities, towns, rural cooperatives— and, if any remains, to private power companies and industries. In 1935 plenty did remain, and $500,000 of current was sold to private companies. The outlet to municipalities has been slow, owing to the desperate legal battle being waged by the power interests. It takes from three to seven years, thousands of dollars and an interregnum of thoroughly bad service for the citizens of any community in this republic to provide themselves with electric power. Efforts of communities in the valley to secure TVA current have been blocked by litigation, injunctions and court decrees, and every penny of the cost of this litigation is paid by citizens in their electric bills to private companies. "The power to delay is the power to destroy."

When the period of impudence, effrontery and sabotage is over, and the way is at last opened, the TVA proceeds to close cooperation with the local town or city. Uniform accounting systems are installed. Power profits are not commingled with tax receipts. A considerate policy is adopted toward the customer. The intention is to give the town all the benefits and services which a private company can give plus a few additional benefits, *without the holding-company milking-machine attachment.* Rates must fall, and a real .yardstick appears. TVA charges are already beginning to rock the rate structure of the region.

It may be objected that rates do not carry an adequate *sales* share of the cost of the dams. The Supreme Court says that the dams are for navigation and flood control and that power is "surplus." If this is true, the power costs nothing, except for the penstock and generator. To my mind such interpretation is a trifle rigorous. If we forget the law and think of the river-basin, it is obvious that these are multiple-purpose dams and the various functions should share the cost, if and when cost accounting is necessary.

Electricity is conceded to be a fine thing. How can poverty-stricken Tennessee farmers pay for it? The TVA's answer is reported by Robert L. Duffus* as follows:

Electricity on the farm is not a luxury but an economy. First you fill your gullies, terrace your land, strip plow your slopes, and let the water flow down as slowly as possible. You collect the water behind dams and produce power. Electricity makes your labor more productive: the one-mule farm becomes an electric farm. You build a big walk-in electric refrigerator, either alone or in cooperation with your neighbors, and in it you store your meat and other perishable products until the market can absorb them at a good price. As your cash income increases you can spend more on your land, on yourself and your family. You will be able to pay your taxes, and your community can support better roads, schools and other public services. The vicious cycle of crop

* *New York Times,* Apr. 19, 1936.

failures, defaulted taxes, poverty and community decay will be reversed.

Public-health work is carried on through the State Health Department and through the long established county agents. Dr. E. L. Bishop is evolving a crucial program of malaria control at the reservoirs, but the contact work is done by local agencies. He has discovered, among other things, that alternate raising and lowering of the reservoir water level about a foot so disturbs the ecology of marine life at the brink that food for mosquito larvae is kept at a minimum, and the pests starve before hatching. He is working out a method for dusting reservoir surfaces by airplane to poison larvae. He has saved $260,000 in the costs of clearing Wheeler reservoir by a new method which also aids the control of mosquitoes.

The story of cooperation with local labor has often been told and I shall review it only briefly. Credit is due primarily to Dr. Arthur E. Morgan. The TVA principle is: Allow no labor conflicts on government jobs; standardize the wage structure; eliminate the peaks and valleys of unemployment; look always at the worker's annual income, for this is what his family lives on, not on a high day rate. Business agents of the unions were at first suspicious. They put on their poker faces and prepared for the usual game of bluff. But the TVA granted collective bargaining at once and invited the agents to assist in preparing the bargaining structure. The policy, every item of which was checked by the unions, was adopted in May, 1935, including full machinery for grievances and wage adjustments. Some 85 per cent of the skilled workers are organized, fifty per cent of the unskilled and ten per cent of the white-collar group. The bluffing game has gone. Both sides lay their cards face up on the table. Norris Dam as a construction job will be a little below the average cost, yet its wages have run from five to twenty per cent above average. There is no sabotage; output per man-hour is high. The accident rate is phenomenally low. Labor throughout the region has been won to the TVA and will fight for its continuance.

All this does not mean that the TVA is on the road to inevitable success. It may be wrecked on various reefs. This merely says that its goal of planning with nature is undeniably sound, that the strategy employed is the only possible one for democratic communities, that the opposition is for the moment in retreat and that visible progress is being made.

In the physical frame of reference, the TVA makes such obvious sense that even a Tory might grasp it. In the pecuniary frame, the case is not so clear. As resources are built up and transformed into crops, industrial products and energy, vested interests in scarcity outside the valley are bound to be alarmed, even though they may have much to gain by the increased prosperity of the region. Their behavior will be in agreement with the behavior of many of our best people today, who are furious because the government spends so much, although the net effect of that spending has been to put them back on their financial feet. Plain facts are no guide in the premises, however. If enough vested interests come to *believe* that the TVA is destined to harm them, they will do their best to put it out of commission. By vested interests I mean farmers beyond the valley as well as industrialists and power companies—indeed all and sundry who fear for their own markets or profits.

The TVA will certainly reach a point in its development when the matter of local industries will have to be squarely met. At present this subject is in the laboratory. One hears of ceramics, canning, sorghum syrups, woodworking and so on. I doubt if the sale of raw materials to the outside world will give enough exchange value to provide really adequate living levels. So the valley will have to take some of its cheap power and manufacture certain goods for its own consumption. Otherwise the whole experiment will hang in mid-air, like a lopsided moon. At this point every manu- facturer of similar commodities outside the valley will cry: "Ho! Help, murder and police!" Let them cry. Too much middle-road technique might end by tempering the project to so many winds that it loses all momentum.

American institutions have changed markedly since 1929, but they must change considerably more before we can enrich our livelihood with forthright, honest regional plan- ning. The TVA, at the present stage of what historians may some day call the Great Transition, must inevitably be a compromise—as the navigation clause which legally justifies it is a compromise—between what is and what is to be.

Compromise or no, to see the authority in operation is a spiritually refreshing experience. To look at the clean, strong walls of Norris Dam between the hills of pine; to feel the will to achievement, the deep integrity of a thousand young- minded men and women, schooled in the disciplines of sci- ence, free from the dreary business of chiseling competitors

286

and advertising soap; to realize that resources are building rather than declining and that the continent is being re-freshed; to know that, over this whole great valley from the Smokies to the Ohio, men's faces turn to a common purpose and a common goal—intoxicates the imagination. Here, struggling in embryo, is perhaps the promise of what all America will some day be.

Chapter XVI

WITH CONSENT OF THE GOVERNED

THE TVA has adopted river-basin planning principles much as we outlined them in Chapter XIV. Nature is the chief consultant. The experiment promises to aid the whole nation, and especially residents of blighted areas. It will present them with carefully developed techniques for reestablishing the resource base and it will teach them to modify the one-crop system in the direction of diversification. It will help them to reduce the cost of that energy upon which modern civilization primarily depends. It will show them how to obtain popular cooperation in their plans, and it will help them to go on living in their own homeland.

Suppose it is desired to improve living levels in a given area. There are three possible approaches:

First, if the area is virgin territory with few people living in it and no vested rights, the planning becomes a straight *engineering* task. Assess the natural resources, design and build the plant, invite the people in. Examples are the Panama Canal Zone, the original city of Washington, St. Petersburg on its Neva swamp, the PWA town of

Matanuska in Alaska, and Radburn, built for the motor age, in New Jersey.

Second, granted an inhabited area, planning may be auto-cratic. Vested interests which object are deported or done away with. People are moved about like chessmen. Prevailing institutions as far as possible are swept aside. The idea is: We are going to take charge of your standard of living whether you like it or not. Examples: Liberia and other large plantation areas in the tropics; parts of Russia, Italy and Germany; coal-company towns in America.

Third, granted an inhabited area, planning may be attempted with the consent of those who live therein. Vested interests are deflected, outgeneraled and not encountered head-on except in critical cases. Prevailing institutions and folkways are carefully reckoned with. There are few dictatorial powers—except in such matters as public health—but rather persuasion, yardsticks, cooperative agreements, intensive education. Examples: Sweden, Norway and Finland; many programs in Great Britain, Australia and New Zealand; the Ontario Hydro and the TVA.

An agricultural plan for the Tennessee Valley which assumed complete state ownership of land and complete mobility of population would be one thing. A plan based on eighty-acre average farms under private ownership would be another. If submarginal and eroded land is defined as nonviable, says John P. Ferris, then hundreds of thousands of people must be moved out of it. But if it is defined as land which can be restored to viability through the efforts of the people themselves, most of them—except those who live in reservoir sites—can stay at home.

289

We must remember, furthermore, that a good deal of American land is marginal because absentee owners control its resources and regard the hinterland as a kind of Belgian Congo. It is not so hopeless physically as the mortgage figures indicate. Large sections of the west are in pawn to New York; much of the south is marginal because northerners own factories and mortgages and skim income from the region. The nation, says David Cushman Coyle, must pay people who work outlying resources enough to make them stay where they are. Otherwise civilization is in full retreat. To keep them there he proposes a stiff income tax collected at the eastern trough and pumped back to resource districts through the medium of public-works expenditures, including conservation. It sounds reasonable enough.

Again, local stability and decentralization are needed even though productive efficiency may not be great, because large-scale industry and business are growing daily more unpredictable. One-crop areas are as dangerous in industry as in agriculture. A new invention comes along and the people of a whole town are left stranded as the factory closes down. We need many diversified, decentralized areas as anchors to windward. The reestablishment of the resource base not only is good for the continent and for the local citizens, but it provides a kind of reservoir against the floods and the droughts of the Great Transition.

Institutions

The limiting factors in planning are human institutions. Plans beyond the capacity of institutions to execute are armchair exercises, suitable for college debates but not for practical action. The zone of possibility is bounded by what people will stand for. We often hear the phrase: "It's a good plan, but it will not work." As Dr. H. S. Person points out, a plan which will not work is no plan at all but idle words in a vacuum. Dictators can act swiftly and directly if the population supports the dictatorial form, or at least does not militantly oppose it. President Roosevelt could act swiftly in the spring of 1933, when a terrified population was willing to surrender nearly every vested right to avoid losing its all in a bottomless depression. As tension relaxed, the administration was obliged to relax the boldness of its projects and temper its program to popular acceptance. American institutions are democratic, not dictatorial, and a president who defied them except in the gravest of emergencies would quickly lose the support of Congress and all power of effective action.

The progressive decline in the resource base is not so dramatic as the decline in paper values enforced by the depression, but in the long run it is more ominous. The assets of a bank are not so valuable as the assets of a watershed. A heap of gold is all but useless, but a running river is a permanent treasure. If and when the American people understand the extent to which nature has been thrust out of equilibrium, and realize the grave penalties attached, it is reasonable to suppose that their institutions will be altered to a point where, with the consent of the governed, effective action can be taken.

Planning under a democratic form of government will never happen simply because it is advisable, or even because the future is at stake. The sovereign voters find their minds taxed to look as much as a month ahead. Meanwhile any new movement for conserving resources is bound to step on somebody's toes. The somebodies are often people with large bank balances, and well organized. They hire distinguished legal talent and repair to Washington, to the courts, to the press, to the telegraph offices and to the microphones until the welkin rings with great injustice done. Widows and orphans hold out their arms before the camera in mute supplication. The nation, choking with sympathetic grief, does nothing. Or if the measure survives the poetic symbol of widows and orphans, the courts put a quietus on it by stretching the due process clause out of its original meaning.

In democratic society real action occurs only when enough people suffer sufficiently to fight for it. Then their concentrated will finds the suffering of vested interests a relatively small obstacle. This is apparently what has happened in the Tennessee Valley. The Grainger Counties are agreeable to change. The outlook under the old dispensation had become black and hopeless.

Ever since the frontier closed Americans have suffered in blighted areas stripped of resources. Wall Street was unconscious of their sufferings. Wall Street has felt some pain itself since 1929, still without realizing that this too had a connection with the land. A decline in resources, coupled with an increase in debt, bears no small responsibility for the depression. Look again at the diagrams in Chapter XIII.

Even people with landed property are beginning to realize by sad experience that, if property is to maintain its value, it must be an item in planned land use. Otherwise upstream owners may ruin it. America could cling to the institution of unregulated private property as long as resources were so extensive that it made little difference to the community what one did with his land or did not do. There was more in the west. When the concept of infinity is punctured, resource planning not only becomes desirable, it becomes institutionally possible. Certainly this has been true throughout western Europe, where conservation is now an accepted institution of the highest legal and social respectability.

Probably a few more stone walls must be encountered before a real advance along the whole front can be taken in America. The encounters will surely come. Meanwhile on various salients substantial advances already have been registered, of which the TVA is an outstanding example.

Who Is Responsible for What?

Let us hope that the tangible experience of the TVA can throw light on a problem which now agitates the nation because of recent Supreme Court decisions. The court is creating dangerous areas of "no man's land." Who is responsible for what? Where does local responsibility give way to state responsibility, to regional responsibility, to federal responsibility? America promises to be flooded with confused litigation until general principles are laid down. The matter will never be settled by consulting the Constitution, but only by objective research.

Suppose a Grainger County has twenty local problems connected with resources. Each is given a number. But 2, 5, 9, 14, 18 and 20 run out of Grainger County into adjoining counties. Problems 5, 9, 14, 18 and 20 run out of the district into the state. Problems 9, 14 and 20 run out of the state into the watershed region. Problems 9 and 20 run out of the region into the nation. If this analysis were made in enough localities, we might have the foundation for a sound legal and political framework.

Small deviations of the Great Wheel—say the matter of supplementary irrigation—can be often met by the individual farmer, larger deviations by a group of farmers getting together in cooperative associations, still larger ones by the town, county, state or regional authority. Great deviations, like floods in the Mississippi basin, demand the executive attention of the federal government. Still other problems— the St. Lawrence waterway for instance—require continental cooperation. Ultimately, for such resources as rare minerals, we must come to world cooperation. What is the problem? Whom does it affect? What political or administrative division is best qualified to cope with it? When these questions are competently answered, the problem approaches solution.

The National Resources Board has made stimulating suggestions along this line. It furnishes a list of ultra-state problems already encountered in its work:

The New York City milk shed, overlapping into Connecticut and New Jersey. (It has been pretty well wrecked as a unit by the Supreme Court.)
Concrete highways and bridges over boundary rivers.
Air lines.
Telephone lines.
Pipe lines.
Railways.

Inland waterways.

Water supply of certain large cities like New York and Los Angeles.

Waste disposal—Chicago and New York.

Recreation facilities—New York and Boston demand and need areas in other states.

Permanent-yield forest areas, often covering more than one state.

Port facilities.

Control of petroleum production.

Transmission lines and power grids.

Labor laws—wages, hours, working conditions.

Detection of criminals.

The New York Planning Commission wonders "whether the entire subject of pollution of interstate waters should not be taken over by the federal government."

The Federal Reserve Banks have been allocated to twelve regions. Altogether there are more than 100 federal regional areas of this type. Some thirty state compacts have been approved by Congress since 1918, covering agreements by two or more states for water control, oil conservation, labor standards and crime prevention. There have been commissions on uniform state laws, conferences of governors, interstate assemblies. Metropolitan planning boards in New York, Chicago, Philadelphia, Washington and St. Louis cross state lines. We have the Pacific Northwest Regional Commission and the New England Planning Commission.

Planning is not a simple matter of Washington versus the states. The states, or parts of them, fall into regions. The most sensible definition of a region from the resource point of view is usually the basin of a great river. If the TVA can find out which functions are local, which belong in the state which belong to the region and which can be settled only by federal action, we shall be profoundly in its debt. The necessity of intelligent distinction grows more pressing every day. If we turn from law books to nature, we can find a real basis for making the distinction. Even the Supreme Court might learn something to its advantage.

Chapter XVII

LAND GUARD

WASHINGTON and Jefferson were good farmers and good conservationists. They checked erosion by contour plowing. John Quincy Adams set aside a forest reserve but Andrew Jackson quashed it. Throughout the nineteenth century lonely scientists and nature lovers raised pen and voice on behalf of the continent but few gave heed. Here and there a sentimental soul was reminded that only God could make a tree, but the solid citizenry was on its way to the woodshed to sharpen the axe. Arbor Day was instituted in Nebraska in 1872. Trees are scarce on the prairies. In 1873 the American Association for the Advancement of Science presented a memorial protesting against forest waste. The first permanent national Forest Reserve was set aside in 1891. The National Academy of Science advocated more reserves in 1897. The Irrigation Division of the Geological Survey began to withdraw reservoir sites on the public domain from private entry late in the '80's.

As the century drew to its close, it was evident that something was in the wind. More protests were heard. In the nineties the frontier closed. The American dream of un-

limited free land was ended. Only cracks and crevices remained to be filled. The concept of infinity lost its raison
d'être, but, as is usual in the majestic courses of history,.
almost nobody was aware of it. America had been a continent where land was abundant and labor and capital scarce;
hence there had been no room in the American language for
the word *conservation*. By 1900 land ceased to be a free good.
Forests, once liabilities and impediments to progress, moved
slowly into the asset column as the supply waned. Even
oil and coal did not look so inexhaustible as was once
assumed. The man-land ratio, to quote Zimmerman, was
maturing.

The time was ripe for a leader to interpret the end of an
epoch and to propose a program. He came. His name was
Theodore Roosevelt, and fortunately he happened to be
President of the United States. He loved the continent, was
a true sportsman and was shrewd enough to read the warning. The butchers, the speculators and the resource wreckers
turned on him with rage and fury. He gave them blow for
blow. With his coworker, Gifford Pinchot, head of the Forest
Service, he put the word *conservation* into the American
dictionary. The actual practice of forestry was begun by the
government in 1905. In 1907 Roosevelt appointed the Inland
Waterways Commission, which began to consider some of
the turns of the Great Wheel. In 1908 he called the famous
White House Conference. It met in the East Room with the
cabinet in attendance, the nine justices of the Supreme Court,
thirty-four governors and delegates from sixty-eight national
societies. It was a landmark. Only a decade had elapsed
between the time it was first seriously needed and the time

it was called. This is rapid work as human institutions go. As a result, the National Conservation Commission was appointed to conduct an inventory of American resources. Its report appeared in 1909, in three large volumes. Mr. Roosevelt did not stop at national boundaries. He excited Canada, Newfoundland and Mexico, and in 1909 requested the powers of the world to meet at the Hague and consider world resources. Had they done so to any purposeful effect, the lives of ten million young men might have been saved a few years later.

One hundred and forty-eight million acres of land were withdrawn from the public domain and converted to federal forest reserves. A million and a half acres on twenty-nine rivers were withdrawn as power sites. Five million acres of phosphate lands in Idaho, Wyoming and Montana were set aside as permanent national property. Altogether 234 million acres were saved from further exploitation by Theodore Roosevelt. The resources of Alaska were permanently protected against ruthless exploitation. It was a good beginning. In subsequent administrations five million acres of oil lands were withdrawn, among them Teapot Dome. The oil companies got their clutches on this pretty property with the help of $100,000 judiciously placed in a little black bag, but Senator Walsh helped to eject them and actually put a wealthy oil man in jail. In 1920 Congress provided that no government lands containing coal, petroleum, gas, shale, phosphate or sodium should ever be sold, though they might be leased. After the White House Conference the states began to march. By 1930 state forests totaled eleven million acres.

The conservation movement inaugurated by Theodore Roosevelt was a little shaky on its facts but it was shrill. It woke us up. We were unduly frightened by statistics of exhaustion which did not take into account improved utiliza-tion. The movement was oversentimental. Little was known at the time about soil depletion and erosion. The hydrologic cycle had not been carefully studied. Regional factors were frequently neglected. The national lumber industry, for instance, might be overexpanded, but a given region would not for that reason prefer the soughing of wind in a primeval forest to the sound of a band saw.

In the generation since the conservation movement was officially inaugurated, many new projects have been under-taken, many new facts gathered, a more intelligent approach worked out. There is less sentiment and more knowledge. Secretary Wilbur was especially devoted to the movement; he pleaded that the public domain be considered in terms of watersheds rather than homesteads. When all was said and done, however, in many brave words and some devoted action, the continent continued steadily to lose its vitality. The movement undoubtedly lessened the rate of decline of certain resources, such as lumber, but it did not halt the decline. The concept of infinity was still strong in men's minds. The grass of the Great Plains remained to be put to the plow. There were war prices to be capitalized. There were booms, and millions to be made from them. The solid citizenry now crossed itself when the word *conservation* was mentioned, but still repaired to the woodlot, axe in hand. All this reflects no discredit on Theodore Roosevelt. He made the most forceful and courageous leader the times could have produced. The historical course had to run a little longer before drastic action could be taken.

In 1929 the economic world turned upside down. By 1933 the social disintegration of America was in plain sight for those who had the hardihood to look. What could not happen was happening. Another Roosevelt was elected president. Under his administration conservation made more progress in three years than during the preceding thirty. Never has the rescue squad been so active. Consider the TVA, which is only one item in the budget. The reasons for this activity are various, but the following impress me as outstanding:

The depression, as we noted earlier, uncovered and dramatized many blighted areas. Something had to be done about them.

Farm prices, falling headlong, produced the triple A, and the triple A focused the attention of the whole nation on problems of agriculture and soil.

Fifteen million unemployed had to be given as many jobs as possible. What could be a more useful job than conserving national resources? The triple C camps presently housed 300,000 young men.

A dry cycle on the plains, followed by dust storms, literally choked the American people into recognition of the tragedy of the grasslands.

The floods of 1936 showed them the other extreme.

New petroleum fields in the early '30's had so disorganized the oil industry that conservation was formally endorsed by all responsible oil companies. The bituminous coal industry was similarly disorganized.

The power gentlemen, headed by Samuel Insull, had over-reached themselves, and an outraged public demanded their control. The readiest form of control was the yardstick technique, using government waters and dams.

Franklin D. Roosevelt, like Theodore Roosevelt, really cared about the continent. He was a country squire, even as Washington and Jefferson. Whatever reservations one may hold about his economics, his politics or his Postmaster General, one cannot fail to appreciate his devotion to land and water. Much of the new impetus given to resource planning is due to his personal interest. Had another been president, the movement would have gained headway because the times demanded it, but hardly to the same degree.

Roll Call

It is instructive to go through the acts of Congress and executive orders bearing on conservation from March, 1933, onward. There are more than thirty acts and thrice as many executive orders. Here is a random sampling:

Acts of Congress

March, 1933. An act to relieve unemployment through useful public work, including forestation, prevention of flood and soil erosion, fire lanes and forest research.

May, 1933. The act creating the Tennessee Valley Authority.

June, 1933. NIRA, including a public-works program for the conservation and development of natural resources.

March, 1934. Fish and game sanctuaries in national forests.

302

March, 1934. Investigation of pollution for better protection of wild-life resources.

June, 1934. Act to conserve and develop Indian lands and resources; restriction of livestock to range capacity.

June, 1934. The Taylor Grazing Act.

February, 1935. Act to conserve petroleum depusits.

April, 1935. Relief appropriation including rural rehabilitation, water conservation, trans-mountain water diversion, CCC camps, soil-erosion work, stream-pollution work, reforestation, flood control, etc. (the famous $4,800,000,000 relief bill, largest in world history).

April, 1935. Conservation of coal, phosphate, oil, shale, gas and sodium on the public domain.

August, 1935. Act to amend the AAA and put it on the basis of soil conservation.

August, 1935. The Guffey coal bill, a major provision of which was coal conservation.

Executive Orders

May, 1933. Twenty million made available for forest lands in twenty states east of the Great Plains.

June, 1933. Helium reserve No. 2 set aside in Utah.

July, 1933. Allocation of NIRA funds to purchase the Great Smoky Mountains National Park.

August, 1933. Federal Power Commission authorized to make extensive water-power survey.

January, 1934. Withdrawal of public lands in Oregon and Washington in connection with Bonneville Dam.

May, 1934. Withdrawal of land for Fort Peck Dam in Montana.

June, 1934. Creation of National Resources Board.

July, 1934. Allocation of fifteen million for planting of trees on famous shelter belt from Gulf to Canada.

July, 1934. Conservation of potash deposits.

December, 1934. Allocation of $5,000,000 for purchase of land in blighted areas; $10,000,000 for CCC. Shelter-belt appropriation revoked.

April, 1935. Resettlement Administration established, including work on erosion, pollution, forestry and flood control.

December, 1935. Migratory waterfowl refuge in Michigan— 24,360 acres of land.

I have picked only a handful out of a barrel. Take the subject of forests alone. From the time of the Weeks Act in 1911 to July 1, 1932, the government established twenty-four new national forests on five million acres of land. In the two years 1933 and 1934, President Roosevelt doubled the area of national forests in the east, and by the middle of 1935 had brought the total area up to sixteen million acres. Soil-erosion work is practically all a product of the present administration. The Taylor Grazing Act, as we noted earlier, revolutionized the policy toward the public domain. "In more ways than one," says Secretary Ickes, "the Taylor Grazing Law is not merely a regulatory measure to upbuild and maintain the public range and to control its use in the interest of stockmen of the nation. It is a Magna Charta upon which the prosperity, well-being and happiness of large sections of this great western country of ours will in the future depend."

It is time and more than time for a coordinated land-use policy to be inaugurated. In the past we have seen the Reclamation Service bringing more crop land into use through irrigation projects, while the AAA had to turn about and eliminate crop land. We have seen the government on the one hand purchasing submarginal land from bankrupt farmers, while on the other permitting homesteading on the public domain, despite the fact "that all lands capable of supporting a family have long since been taken up"—thus creating more bankrupts. The new land policy according to Secretary Ickes provides that, "when an acre of land is brought into cultiva' tion as the result of reclamation or drainage, acreage of sub' marginal land of an equivalent productive capacity shall be taken out of cultivation and turned back either into the public domain or into national forests."

The whole federal government is replete with conserva' tion projects and agencies. Mr. Ickes proposes that the name of the Department of the Interior be changed to the Depart' ment of Conservation. There is a planning commission operating in every one of the forty-eight states, largely concerned with land and water problems. A number of regional agencies have been set up, as we have seen. Congress' men like Maury Maverick of Texas pledge their careers to conservation. Governor Marland of Oklahoma recently told me that with one-third of the land of his state ruined by erosion, no question was of more vital concern. Among the most impressive federal agencies now working on these problems are the following:

The Soil Conservation Service.

The Tennessee Valley Authority.

The National Resources Board (now Committee). A planning division only, author of a series of very fine reports.

The new AAA. Agricultural relief shifted to a conservation basis.

The Resettlement Administration. Struggling with the problem of blighted areas.

The Rural Electrification Administration.

305

. The Public Works Administration. Long- and short-term conservation projects, water supply, pollution control, drainage, etc.

The CCC camps. Forestry and erosion work.

The Works Progress Administration.

The Forest Service.

The Biological Survey. Concerned with wild-life protection.

The Geological Survey. Mapping, planning, minerals.

The Reclamation Service. Greatest of dam builders. Irrigation problems.

The last four are divisions with long and honorable histories; all the rest are new since 1933. It would take a regiment of accountants to determine annual expenditures now devoted to conservation as such, but the total certainly exceeds a billion dollars. This means work for probably a million men. The largest outlays are for the purchase of forest and submarginal lands, the TVA dams, the new AAA payments for conservation, the projects of the Resettlement Administration, the CCC and the public-works projects. In earlier chapters attention has been repeatedly called to one or another aspect of the federal rescue squad. We have already given a chapter to the TVA and could well give a whole book to the other divisions. It would make stimulating reading for all who value their country. We have space to describe but a few of the services here.

The Soil Conservation Service

Originally set up in the Department of the Interior, the service has been transferred—not, unfortunately, without some hard feeling—to the Department of Agriculture. It is

carrying on about 600 demonstration projects on approximately 55 million acres of land. It operates thirteen control
experiment stations and forty-one nurseries. It directs 455
CCC camps in their work to control erosion. The theory of
the service is to plant many local centers which can spread
to surrounding areas. A demonstration project is set up
where neighboring farmers may inspect it critically. The
TVA uses the same method in its county demonstration
stations. In 1935 the Soil Conservation Service estimated
that at least 250,000 farmers had been exposed to these
sample projects. No compulsion is attempted. Demonstra-
tions on private land, of which there are more than 130, are
purely voluntary. Let us examine one of them near Americus,
Georgia, which I visited on my expedition to the stupendous
gullies of Stewart County.

The drainage area of Muckalee Creek, comprising about
40,000 acres, had been selected for a station. The land is
rolling country on the coastal plain, originally wooded, and
now devoted primarily to cotton, corn and peanuts. Little
livestock has been raised. Remaining woodlots have been
mercilessly burned over in the vain hope of exorcising boll
weevils. Sheet erosion is severe on all slopes over seven
per cent. There are few large gullies, but many from three
to eight feet deep on the steeper slopes. One sees their red
scars on every side. About half the crop land in the area
has been terraced at one time or another, but the work has
been inadequate, without proper outlets for water.

Some 200 farms are located in the basin. At the time of
my visit, 130 farmers had signed contracts with the conservation service. About sixty per cent are owners and forty

per cent tenants. Seven individuals are negroes. The first step was to call a meeting and explain the project, this in the early part of 1935. Then the farmers were invited to sign contracts undertaking to cooperate with the service for a definite length of time. I was told that only one man had dropped out after signing.

Farmer Brown, for instance, signs up. A careful map of his farm is prepared. He and an expert go to work on it and the result will be their joint endeavor. Slopes are classified A, B, C and D—the latter being twelve per cent or over. All D slopes must be taken out of crops. This steep slope had best go to pine, that one to grass or pasture; this field may remain in crop. A plan for rotation is evolved, considering local market conditions. Woodland management is worked out and possibilities are calculated for future income from turpentine, pulpwood and saw timber. Fire is considered and its evils carefully explained. The expert suggests what to plant in this or that gully on Mr. Brown's farm. Will honeysuckle grow fast enough or had they better use kudzu vine? This deep gully needs a thicket of black locust.

When Mr. Brown and the service man reach an agreement, a platoon of CCC boys comes in, also WPA workers, bringing seeds, fertilizers and special Diesel tractor terracers. The farmer on his part contributes labor, mulch and such supplies as he has available. Crop lands are effectively terraced by a drag scoop specially shaped for sloping ground and drawn by a red tractor. It makes beautiful curved furrows along the contours. The CCC boys in this district are negroes from Atlanta who three years ago had never seen a crosscut saw. They go after the gullies with cement dams,

PLATE XIII.—Terracer at work. (*Courtesy of Caterpillar Tractor Company.*)

lumber dams, kudzu vine and seedling pine, and they build neat channels lined with concrete to drain the terraces. Since they have been in camp these boys have gained an average of twenty pounds each. I used to pass them on the way to work in truckloads, singing lustily. Meanwhile along the roadsides old negro women were carefully planting trees, at $22 a month on the WPA.

It is impressive to compare a protected farm where work has been in progress for a year and more with an unprotected one across the rail fence. Here are neat terraces, gullies filling up, concrete ditches, new grass, little long-leaf pine trees feathering the slopes; there red, raw gullies, finger erosion above them, with furrows running down all kinds of slopes. The more prosperous farmers are likely to sign contracts first, but their neighbors who used to scoff are now signing up too. "See that slope there, how nice those terraces came out? Pretty, ain't it? And that new grass. Those cows are new. Yes, sir, you wouldn't recognize this farm. And we're getting more cash income for less labor." The Kiwanis Club has offered a prize of $50 for the best essay on erosion by local school children. A big model has been prepared, such as one sees at world's fairs, showing the same farm protected and unprotected, with houses, barns, fences, gullies, cotton, grass, cows, all complete. Tiny electric lights illuminate the several talking points. It is carried around in a truck to high schools, farmers' meetings, Main Street gatherings. All this, if you please, in darkest Georgia.

The Soil Conservation Service has made the first comprehensive survey of the extent of erosion in the United

States. The figures quoted earlier in this book are largely taken from that survey. It works on erosion by wind as well as by water, and it works in the laboratory as well as in the field. The staff, like that of the TVA, is keen, competent and inspired with a magnificent goal.

Let us follow Mr. H. H. Bennett, chief of the service, on a recent swing around the circuit in the west. His account is full of horrible examples and heroic recoveries. In the Palouse wheat region of the far northwest, for instance, conditions have been very bad. Six years ago farmers laughed at erosion control. The models and propaganda were introduced. "Now the countryside is erosion conscious." Many highly erosible fields are being planted to combinations of sweet clover, alfalfa and grass. On the watershed above Pullman, 10,000 acres sown to grass and taken out of wheat have saved a billion and a half gallons of runoff hitherto wasted. Tractors used to run in zigzags to avoid gullies. Now they can attend to business. Behind the new control dams, pools of water are collecting, the underground water table is rising, wild ducks are breeding again "along ravines that only a little while ago were dry as desert arroyos all summer long." Much of the land plowed to wheat is so steep that harvesting machinery had to be fitted with special balancing devices lest it tip over. Here and there bedrock thrust through the soil. Now these slopes are going back to grass and forest, with a limited number of sheep on the grass.

In the Arroyo Grande district in southern California, land once worth up to $1,000 an acre lies abandoned, topsoil gone, "farmed to death." Lowlands worth an equal sum have been covered with debris from above, many to the

depth of ten feet of sand. A fence is buried, another is built
on top of it, and the second is buried—sometimes a third.
All this occurred within ten years; cultivation did not begin
until 1925. With the help of the service, farmers have gone
to work on the desolation. One huge gully cost $10,000 to
fill, but it saved $200,000 worth of threatened land. In the
Las Posas district fruit trees have been planted on 30-degree
slopes with careful contour plowing. "Land thus treated
lost no soil and very little water during a single cloudburst
in 1934, when similar untreated plowed slopes lost 500 tons
of soil per acre." In the Navajo project at Mexican Springs,
50,000 acres are being rescued from the ravages of overgrazing. In the dust bowl of the Texas Panhandle, the rescue
squad is nailing down the moving dunes with sorghum,
sudan grass and small grain cover. The region around Huron,
South Dakota, is going out of wheat and back to pasture.
Mr. Bennett sees a twenty-five-year job ahead, but he is
hopeful.

Resettlement

The TVA is trying to reestablish the resource base of the
Tennessee Valley. The Resettlement Administration is
making the same attempt in blighted areas from coast to
coast. In the first case one sees unity, integration and excellent administration, built around the great dams. In the
second case one sees diversity, lack of integration and an
administration which has not yet found itself. The reasons
are not far to seek. The Resettlement Administration fell
heir to an extraordinary litter of subsistence homestead
projects, rural rehabilitation corporations and plain starva-

tion areas, covering all kinds and conditions of people and resources and located in nearly every state in the union.

The subsistence homesteads were pretty to look at but the factor of a permanent exchange base had not been carefully worked out. How were the residents in their pretty cottages to pay their cash bills? The cumulative wreckage of decades of resource neglect fell upon the heads of Rexford Tugwell and his aides. Occasionally they come up for air, but mostly they are submerged under a difficult, complicated and extremely necessary task. Theirs is the job of trying to find livelihood again for the people of the Dust Bowl and the cut-over areas, for the swamp-drainage victims, for the erosion victims, for the exhausted mining villages, for the whole gray, beaten army who try to live on submarginal lands. When you think of an eloquent and indignant phrase to fling at Mr. Tugwell and his boondoggling administration, stop and remember this: In our mad rush to subdue a continent we have stranded and broken these people—millions of them. Is it wild extravagance, red radicalism from Moscow, to give them a hand and try to put them on their feet?

The administration has ten million acres of marginal land under option for purchase and is operating some 250 projects in 470 counties. Its active pay roll numbers 31,000 employees.

Here is a typical project—Sublimity Forest in the Kentucky mountains. A scattered population sought to wring a living from the mountain coves and valleys of this area, until the agricultural outlook became hopeless. So the Resettlement Administration in cooperation with the Forest Service undertook an experiment. They selected sixty men known to be good forest workers and established

them with their families in an area where the soil is productive. Each family will have three or four acres, a cow and
access to common pasture ground. Houses are being built
and rented on reasonable terms. The bulk of the food supply
will be raised in the family garden and a little surplus may
be sold in the neighboring town of Landon. To this point
we have the typical subsistence homestead. It is totally
inadequate as a solution to anything. Let us proceed. *Each
family head is to be guaranteed a cash income of $300 a year for
six months' work in the woods.* Sublimity Forest is to be put
on a permanent-yield basis, under the expert management
of the Forest Service, which has been doing this kind of
work for thirty years. Cutting will go on forever, as annual
growth will always equal the cut. Each family has its
garden, a well-built house rented for about one-sixth of its
income and a job for life—a useful and necessary job. If
the project proves successful, it can be applied all over the
Kentucky mountain area, where the government already
owns six million acres of forest land.

The Forest Service

Napoleon, when the battle wavered, threw in the Old
Guard, the seasoned troops. In the same way the Forest
Service is the seasoned corps which stiffens, instructs and
frequently salvages the errors of the green new armies of
conservation. It has been through the wars for a generation,
ever since Gifford Pinchot first led it into battle. It bolsters
the CCC camps, the erosion services, the TVA, the
public-works brigades, the Resettlement Administration in
Sublimity Forest and elsewhere. It writes reports for the

313

National Resources Board. It helps lead many Indians back into their ancient way of life, where they are happier than in tin-roofed bungalows trying to keep up with the Joneses. One cannot go far in any conservation service without encountering a forester, and a feeling of—how shall I put it?—stability.

The Forest Service must know its stuff. It has the biggest tree job in the world. It is responsible for the management of 160 million acres of forest land. It cuts a billion feet of timber a year. Eight million head of cattle are grazing on its domain. It is fighting fires not only in its own vast empire but in all American forests. Seven hundred cities and towns are dependent on its forests for their water supply. Twenty million people take advantage of its recreation facilities every year. Like the Coast Guard, the Forest Service attracts a superior type of human being, a happy combination of woodsman and scientist. It is fitting that the Forest Service laboratory at Madison, Wisconsin, should be one of the most beautiful examples of modern architecture in the world.

CCC

President Roosevelt had hardly got the banks opened when he haled 300,000 youths from depression street corners into the woods. To date more than a million have received the discipline of the Civilian Conservation Corps. In two years these young men have:

Built 48,000 miles of truck roads for fighting fires.
Built 35,000 miles of fire brakes.

314

PLATE XIV.—GULLY CONTROL CREW. (*Photo by T.V.A. Staff.*)

Built 43,000 miles of fire telephone lines.

Removed inflammable underbrush from 1,038,000 acres.

Carried on erosion work on 1,916,000 acres.

Built 1,400,000 check dams in gullies.

Spent 1,700,000 man-days fighting fires.

Planted 267,000,000 trees.

Improved the forest stand on 1,644,000 acres.

Fought plant diseases on 4,000,000 acres.

Attacked rodents on 11,000,000 acres.

Built 1,688 lookout towers for fighting fire.

Driven 4,750 wells.

Spent 80,000 man-days obliterating dumps.

Razed 1,779 unsightly structures.

Fought mosquitoes on 43,000 acres.

Spent 73,800 man-days practising tree surgery.

Restocked waters with 49,000,000 fish.

Spent 16,500 man-days in archeological work.

Devoted 23,000 man-days to rescuing persons in flood, fire, accident and calamity.

The value of the work done in this period has been estimated at 400 million dollars. This is a by-product, for the boys are not working in the calculus of profit and loss. While performing these services they have gained an average of seven pounds each, and their death rate has dropped from eight per 1,000 on poolroom corners to two per 1,000 in the woods. They have tackled and completed tasks which foresters, in 1932, never dreamed could be accomplished for fifty years. They have dramatized conservation as no other service has done and have proved by tangible performance that defending the continent is, so far as it goes, the best cure for unemployment.

315

The New AAA

It is too early to have an opinion about the effectiveness of the legislation which was hastily pushed through Congress after the Supreme Court had killed the original Agricultural Adjustment Administration. One can simply state that the Court left a vacuum, which, if not promptly filled, would have invited a serious explosion, and that Congress, the farm leaders and the Department of Agriculture did their best. Perhaps their best is not good enough. Secretary Wallace has his doubts. Let us hear what he believes the act will do.*

In 1930, of the 400 million acres of tilled land in America, 300 million acres was in soil-depleting crops and 100 million in soil-building crops, such as grass and legumes. The act proposes to shift thirty million acres from depleting to building crops, which will give 270 million acres of the former and 130 million of the latter. For the ten years prior to 1930, 270 million acres supplied all our *domestic* market demand for food and fiber. The balance, thirty million acres, furnished food and fiber for export. The export business has largely gone, so the shift now proposed will not cut into the domestic supply. The soil-depleting crops—cotton, corn, wheat and tobacco—were also the export crops. Farmers will receive some 500 million dollars a year for making the shift. It is all voluntary; the Supreme Court has banned the making of contracts. For those of you who have followed me thus far, I do not need to emphasize what thirty million acres of new grasslands and soil-building crops will mean to the continent.

Will the farmers cooperate without contracts, or will they try to beat the gun and ship the maximum to market while

* In the *New York Times*. Mar. 29, 1936.

prices are relatively good? Mr. Wallace does not know, and neither do I. But we agree that, if they do not cooperate, American agriculture will find itself in the impasse of 1932, when prices were falling toward the center of the earth.

The rescue squad is hard at work on a score of fronts, federal, regional, state and local. It can be justly criticized for lack of coordination, for overlapping services here and there, for certain plans based on inadequate factual surveys, for many examples of inefficiency. But one consideration stands head and shoulders above the need for consolidation and better executive detail. The administration at Washington has accepted the fact that America is no longer adolescent—booming and boosting its way into an incredible future where growth curves never level off. It accepts maturity—is done with the concept of infinity. It believes that the time has come to replenish the physical assets of a continent worn and ravaged by centuries of adolescent carelessness and misuse. It is acting on that belief with a billion dollars and a million men.

No more exciting and rewarding work is going on anywhere in America. I speak of all the forces of conservation, administration or nonadministration. These services are fighting for our homeland, attacking enemies as destructive as invading armies from beyond the seas. They are the Land Guard. Whether they have yet halted the progressive deterioration of three centuries, I cannot say; I can merely affirm that they are the right means and the only means to do so. Those who would stop this work do so at their peril. The account will be settled, not by men, by political administrations or by laws and speeches, but by nature.

Chapter XVIII

FIVE MILLION JOBS

EVERY year in America a million youngsters graduate from high school and college to enter the employment market. Since 1929 there has been no market worthy of the name. The Youth Administration estimates that there are in the country today upward of five million young people between sixteen and twenty-five who are not at school and who have no occupation. Despite a certain amount of business recovery since the depression low, there are still more than ten million unemployed. Despite learned studies which conclude that there is no such thing as technological unemployment, the fact remains that a man-hour of labor costs a manufacturer perhaps fifty cents; a kilowatt-hour of energy costs him perhaps one cent. The kilowatt will do ten times as much work as the man, never gets tired, never talks back and never joins a labor union. As America matures, industry will use kilowatts increasingly and will not have the need for man power which it had in the past.

What are the unemployed to do? What are these million new candidates a year to do? What are your own children to do when they graduate? You have saved and skimped to provide them with educational advantage. Where is the opportunity?

The National Resources Board finds plenty of opportunity for your children. Waiting to be done, at current prices, is 105 billion dollars worth of work in the division of public business—from three and a half to five billion dollars a year for the next twenty to thirty years. This means roughly three to four million jobs. The old gentlemen with the gold watchchain in the front row appears to be having a heart attack. "Where's the money coming from?" he gasps. In the next chapter we will answer him. Meanwhile let the usher bring him a drink of water. We are operating at this point in the physical frame of reference and we propose to record tasks which need doing on behalf of the continent and of the community generally. If Wall Street can find no way to finance necessary labor, we should look for a new breed of financial wizards.

The budget of the Resources Board covers improvements to 1,750,000 miles of dirt roads, the elimination of 5,000 especially dangerous grade crossings (to eliminate all grade crossings would cost 12 billions), eight billion dollars for flood and drainage basin projects, housing for the lower income groups, water supply and sewage, rural electrification and so on.

Now I am about to say something that may cause the most forward looking of you to shake his head doubtfully and the old gentleman in the front row to swoon away. When there is a large reserve of unemployed, public works cost nothing. Zero. If we had been properly educated, we should say, "Of course! Tell us something not so trite and obvious." But having been brought up in a fantastic money economy, we cannot look at the world outside and see it straight. The prohibitions are in our heads, not in the nature of things. Cost in the last analysis always comes back to human labor. As an accountant I can prove this on any set of books you care to give me. Unemployed citizens in civilized communities must be kept alive. Putting these two propositions together, it follows that the unemployed might better be doing something useful in their spare time.

The National Resources Board runs down the list of those activities which used to create employment after a depression, when the country was still growing up:

Commercial and Factory Construction.—Now checkmated because of general excess capacity.

Home Building.—Checkmated for lower income groups because of low incomes. "The government must help if housing is to absorb many new workers."

Railroads.—A declining industry. There is some call for new equipment, but nothing like that which obtained in the old days of expansion.

Steel.—It is doubtful whether the steel industry will much exceed its 1929 output because of new metals and alloys. There is also a large increase in labor-saving devices.

Foreign Trade.—Economic nationalism is on the horizon for the indefinite future. No more new employment is to be expected here.

New Inventions.—There are some possibilities in this department. Prefabricated housing, however, the likeliest candidate, will create many new factory jobs, but will wreck the building trades.

Decentralization of Industry.—It may create a little additional building activity.

Subsistence Homesteads and Self-help Enterprises.—"An inefficient makeshift pending the restoration of normal activity.'

"In general wholesale reduction of unemployment cannot be achieved in the next year or two—probably not in five years—by promotion of new products or new principles of industrial organization."

If we turn, however, from the activities of adolescence to the activities of maturity, we find jobs opening on every hand. In addition to the budget presented by the Resources Board, certain specialists at Washington were asked to present estimates of the man power required to bring soils and forests back to par under an "ideal program." Here is their reply:

	Number of men, full time	
	Restoration and development (ten year program)	Continuing work in protection and management
Soil conservation on farm lands..........	400,000	To be done by farmers
Nonfarm woodlands..................	94,000	330,000
Parks................................	—	19,000
Grasslands, etc........................	23,000	22,000
Total	517,000	371,000

In other words, the experts saw useful work for 517,000 men in bringing lands back over the next ten years; then, when restoration was accomplished, permanent jobs for

371,000 men. For ten years, the total work required would be 888,000 man-years per year, or 1,776,000 half-time jobs. The latter is the better method, for much of the work is seasonal. We remember the project in Sublimity Forest in Kentucky where men worked in their gardens and around the home for part of the year, and in the woods earning cash income for the balance. Here are nearly two million cash jobs for those who have homes and gardens in rural areas. This is the type of part-time occupation peculiarly adapted to those living in marginal lands. The experts estimated that 75 per cent of the tasks would be unskilled, 15 per cent technical and skilled, 10 per cent administrative. Thus there are more than 200,000 jobs available for college and high-school graduates—25 per cent of 888,000.

Another group of specialists in water resources was asked for an ideal national program. They submitted estimates covering pollution control, stream improvements, flood control, irrigation and hydroelectric power.

Total cost...............................	$5,500,000,000
First-year cost...........................	$1,100,000,000
Total man-hours, first year..................	875,000,000
Approximate jobs, first year.................	440,000
Unskilled jobs (47 per cent)................	207,000
Semiskilled jobs (22 per cent)..............	97,000
Skilled jobs (19 per cent)..................	83,000
Professional jobs (5 per cent)..............	22,000
Administrative jobs (7 per cent)............	31,000

The National Resources Board has submitted a careful plan for the control of pollution in the Potomac River. The man-hours involved for capital outlay are as follows:

Sewage-treatment plants	7,199,000
Industrial-waste treatment	3,324,000
Conservancy dams	1,090,000
Sealing coal mines	170,000
Investigations	200,000
Administration	800,000
Total	12,783,000

The Mississippi Valley Committee after voluminous investigation finds that the federal government could profitably spend one billion dollars in the next twenty years on river works in the Mississippi Valley, half of them self-liquidating power installations. Another 100 million could be well spent for self-liquidating rural electrification lines, another 940 million for acquisition and improvement of forests, another 400 million for control of erosion over a twenty-year period.

Of three million square miles in America, only 810,000 or twenty-seven per cent is covered by adequate topographical maps. Here is a ten-year task, costing $117,000,000, literally crying to be done. Adequate maps are the basis of adequate land planning. In addition—listen well, young technical graduates—the National Resources Board calls for aerial mosaic photographs of many areas, such as the TVA is now using to great advantage, for climatology surveys, for soil and surface surveys, for vegetation studies, for laboratory studies in natural regeneration after destructive exploitation, for studies in degenerative vegetational succession and in genetics of domesticated plants, for the mapping of population distribution.

We pointed out in an earlier chapter that 380 million dollars is required to give adequate protection to the urban population against water pollution. Present irrigation systems are woefully short of dependable water. They need an additional 86 million acre-feet of storage to keep them functioning in dry years. The national loss due to pests has been assessed at two billion dollars a year. The CCC boys have begun the assault on vermin, but there is room for more regiments. As noted earlier, America is short of antimony, chromite, nickel, tin, manganese, mercury, tungsten and certain other minerals. The National Resources Board suggests that a thorough search be made for possible deposits, using the latest geophysical prospecting methods and instruments. The Russians are far ahead of us in scientific explorations of this character and have added greatly to their resource inventory in the past few years. It is fascinating work, much of it in the field, requiring the highest type of technical skill.

It is instructive to summarize the reports submitted by local communities when the WPA relief project was launched. A questionnaire was addressed to them asking what useful local work was in order. Replies were received from 21,200 states, counties, cities, towns and school districts, proposing 137,000 projects at an estimated cost of $20,336,000,000. By percentage of total estimated cost, the replies fell in the order shown in the table on page 325. Some boondoggling, undoubtedly, and much fine, useful work.

The State of Wisconsin, under Governor La Follette, has developed a detailed plan for public works to be spread over ten years, from 1936 to 1946. The total runs to 392 millions, or about 40 millions a year—say upward of 30,000 jobs.

The plan is worked out county by county, and includes not only man-hour costs but also the specific trades and professions which will be needed—common labor, brick-layers, carpenters, roofers, plasterers, painters, plumbers, electricians, engineers and so on. The largest single item is highway improvement, but others are watershed develop-ment, forest laboratories, control of forest fires, erosion work, parks, fish hatcheries, water-supply, sewage works and recreation facilities. The plan, it should be pointed out, is not "ideal," but exceedingly practical. Detail has been developed to such a degree that work can be started to-morrow. Some of it has started. No other state, to my knowl-edge, has prepared such comprehensive plans based on exhaustive factual surveys.*

WPA *Proposed Projects*

	Per Cent
Roads and highway improvements	22.0
Reclamation, flood control, power	14.5
Water supply and sanitation	11.5
Buildings, other than schools	9.0
Bridges, tunnels, wharves, etc.	8.0
Transport facilities	7.7
School buildings and equipment	6.6
Grade crossings	5.0
Utilities	4.0
Recreation facilities	3.2
Miscellaneous (airports, navigation, pest control, surveys)	8.5
Total	100.0

The above are samples of the paper work already com-pleted for the real work which lies ahead. In soil conserva-tion alone one highly placed expert believes that the bulk

* Regional Plan Report, 1934, 501 pages.

of the unemployed could be put to work at tasks requiring every variety of skill. If we were really determined to bring the continent back to par in ten or twenty years' time, there is no question in my mind that all the present idle plus all future additions to their ranks from technological causes or otherwise could find constructive work.

Recreation

As kilowatts supersede man-hours, human labor will be devoted increasingly to services rather than to physical production. Take the matter of recreation alone. It is primarily a service function, and its extent is already enormous. The sedentary occupations of modern civilization demand recreation to maintain the human balance. Shorter working hours demand recreation. The National Resources Board finds that forty per cent of the people now live on 0.002 per cent of the land. In the Rocky Mountain states, three per cent live on twenty-eight per cent of the land. An acre is required for every 100 city people for recreational purposes, but less than half of that is now available. In 1915 national parks had 335,000 visitors; in 1935, four million. This is due in part to the rise of the motorcar and in part to the rise in demand for recreation.

Scenery, like cotton, is a crop which cannot be enjoyed without the expenditure of labor. People come to the Rockies, the lake country of Michigan, the New England coast, Florida, California and the Great Smokies to buy scenery as they buy food from other areas. The customers must be served. Scenery is the resource base of these sections, as we pointed out earlier, and needs planning for its preserva-

326

tion just as Grainger County needs planning. Commercial interests will ruin the crop with the same expedition shown elsewhere. I can show you a dozen spots about New York which were once lovely with lake, hill and meadow, now turned into rural slums, foul with bungalows heaped together, with dancehalls, twenty-foot signboards, lunch wagons, gas stations, polluted water and roadhouses taste-fully shaped like ice cream cones! Without regulation, scenery is often reduced to a shambles, game is killed off, streams are fished out, woods are burned by careless campers. Nothing of value remains.

Sir Francis Younghusband, the famous British explorer, once said that nature was at its best under two conditions: completely virginal and wild like the Himalayas or Alaska; completely controlled and tended as in an English country estate. We need many wilderness areas in America where men may refresh themselves after cranking the levers of adding machines. Recreation, like soil, if it is to be a perma-nent asset, can provide hundreds of thousands of useful jobs. Go to Bear Mountain Park on the Hudson, run by the state of New York, and see the type of work required and its enduring value. Then go to Lake Mahopac and see a horrible contrast.

The various proposals for future work set forth above simply carry forward tasks on which the rescue squad is already engaged. There is nothing new or theoretical about the idea. Today more than 700,000 men, 90 per cent of them relief workers, are in the woods, according to the Forest Service. The TVA watershed controls, the erosion projects of the Soil Conservation Service, the National Park Service and hundreds of municipal drainage and water-supply projects are actually going on. In resource reconstruction alone, well over a million workers are now engaged. Walk around any town and somewhere you will see the dirt flying. Improved administrative techniques are being rapidly developed. Historians of the future may regard Mr. Harry Hopkins as one of the world's greatest administrators. We do not here propose an untried scheme, but only more of what is actually in operation, and a shift of emphasis from a temporary depression-lifting attack to a permanent continent-saving attack.

Public works, it must be remembered, are not all on the expenditure side. Many are self-liquidating, like housing, lumbering, rural electrification, power production. Many pay part of their own way, like highways, water and sewage systems and parks and playgrounds where small fees are charged. From the point of view of the financial system which is to come, self-liquidation will be no virtue. The cardinal questions will be whether the service rebuilds the capital assets of the country and whether it produces current wealth—as in housing.

Finally, let us examine a curious paradox. The National Resources Board reports that the most persistent suggestion of state planning commissions is to put city unemployed on the land. A patch of ground, a vine and fig tree, rosy-cheeked children gathering buttercups, the simple virtues—and no more queues in front of employment bureaus on State Street. One fears that the suggestion is persistent because planning commissions live in cities, and city folks generally want to get the unemployed out of sight and out of mind. So a pleasant bucolic fiction is invented.

Out in the country, with resource base shattered or with wheat being burned for fuel, the persistent suggestion is to secure a factory job. The Minnesota commission is frank to say that an influx of city unemployed would only give the farmer more competition and trouble. Under current financial arrangements there is a surplus of farmers. There may even be an actual surplus in terms of the capacity of the American stomach. So city authorities would throw surplus factory workers on the farm, and rural authorities would throw surplus farmers into the factory—an unimaginative run-around. The vicious circle is actually in vigorous rotation at the present time. It can be broken only by taking both surplus factory labor and surplus farmers and putting them to work reclaiming resources, producing tangible wealth in public works and services and so gradually building a demand which will stimulate the output of remaining farmers and factory workers. *There is no other solution for unemployment in a maturing economy.* Perhaps it would be better to say that there is no other *principle* upon which a solution may be founded. There are various methods— some known and some to be discovered—of putting the principle into practical effect. But no method, I am afraid, will satisfy the old gentleman in the front row. He was conditioned in a swiftly growing country, he believes in the concept of infinity, and the practical problems of maturity are too much for him altogether.

A Glance Ahead

In Ducktown we saw the future of America in the event of a decision to let the trends of the past continue unaltered.

What will America look like if it is decided to reverse those trends? Go to Sweden today and look about you for a rough picture. Or look at our own national parks. In place of dying cut-over lands, great living wilderness areas will be preserved for those who would rather walk and paddle than drive a car. The Brook Trail on Chocorua will wind forever through primeval forest. Submarginal areas will be deserted save for their resource guardians. Communities will gradually become permanent and more compact. Restless migration will give way to settled areas, where homes may go on for generations. A good norm for rural communities is 10,000 people living within easy driving distance of a market center. This gives opportunity for adequate schools, roads, stores, entertainment and other community services.

There will be fewer heavily industrialized centers and more local industry. The west and south will manufacture a larger fraction of the goods they consume. No community will be self-sufficient, but all communities will become more nearly self-supporting than at present, less vulnerable to financial somersaults in Chicago and New York. One-industry towns, like one-crop farms, will tend to disappear. Cities will shrink in size. Slums will become as great an anachronism as human slavery. Automatic mills and factories will be the general rule, for the continent will be drenched with power—even as Steinmetz foresaw. There will be

330

a tremendous decline in smoke, dirt and noise. In spite of autogiros, life will be more leisurely; and because of them, roads will be less dangerous and congested.

Buffalo grass will be waving again over most of the Great Plains, supporting a supportable load of cattle and sheep. Vegetation will lay the sands of the Dust Bowl. There will be water in the potholes and the flyways will be alive with birds. Trout will leap in a thousand streams. The north woods will be full of moose, deer and bear. Destructive floods will be a rarity, droughts far less calamitous. Water will run clear and sweet to the sea. Old Man River will get off his artificial stilts and sink to his once-comfortable bed. A hundred great reservoirs will sparkle in the river basins, holding the floods, producing cheap power, providing boating, bathing, camping and fishing. Look again at the plans for Norris Forest. Crop lands will probably decline, with some giant mechanized farms where technical and natural conditions warrant and many prosperous small holdings operated by their owners, well supplied with power, little reservoirs and supplementary irrigation. The Central Valley of California, artesian basins full, will be prepared to furnish apples, grapes and onions to perpetuity. Stewart County will have become a national park. American Indians, their broad forests and grazing lands protected to perpetuity, will at last find peace in the ways of their fathers.

Occupations will probably fall into five major classes:

Full-time work in industry or commerce.
Full-time farming.
Full-time work in resource maintenance or other public service.

331

Part-time work for money in forestry, soil building, conservation, local seasonal industries (like canning), combined with food growing in home gardens and some home craftsmanship.

Professional work as heretofore, with large increases in personnel, and far more demand for research, planning and expert public administration.

Service trades will expand, especially in the fields of education, recreation and culture. During the period of reconstruction, hours of work will remain much as they average today. After the resource base has been reestablished, hours will decline. Unemployment will become as rare as in colonial New England. The town dump will smoulder no longer, water fronts will be clean and welcoming, gas tanks will have been melted down for scrap, and from the Bay of Fundy to the mighty bridge at the Golden Gate no billboard will dare to raise its head.

Utopia? Wish fulfillment? The picture would fulfill perhaps my dearest personal wish, and that of thousands of others. Are the desires of citizens never to register in this democracy? They have registered in Sweden, as you can see by using your eyes rather than your prejudices.

But the picture is far more than personal desire. It is the logical end of work already begun. It is the only way to reconcile the two great realities which affect our lives. It is the pattern for working with nature while accepting the great gifts of the power age.

Chapter XIX

TO SAVE A CONTINENT

Where Is the Money Coming From?

AMERICAN expenditures are now destined to be those of a maturing culture, rather than those of an economy that has been expanding for a century and more at a five per cent compound interest rate. Expansion commenced to decline in 1910, but it took a monster depression twenty years later to drive the fact home. As a people we stand perplexed and frustrated when the rhythm which conditioned us changes. Old gentlemen become apoplectic; industrial and financial tycoons hire expensive experts with charts and diagrams to prove that expansion at the old rate will continue indefinitely.

The financial system as we have known it was kept in reasonable equilibrium by devoting savings to new capital expansion. When maturity cries a halt, the savings accumulate in sterile lumps and choke the system. A pulmotor is then applied in the form of infusions of bank credit, based on expectations of future expansion. This device kept us afloat during the New Era—thirty billions of bank-credit inflation. The infusion creates temporary purchasing power

333

on the one hand and debt on the other. The debt is a gamble on future growth at the old rate. If growth does not materialize, the debt ultimately ceases to have value, although it may be maintained on the books for a time by various expedients. The Reconstruction Finance Corporation and other government credit agencies maintained old debt by issuing new debt against it. Obviously this but postpones a final settlement.

The traditional savings-spendings formula has been thrown completely out of gear.* If maturity is a fact, there is no way of making the formula function again. We simply cannot use more factories, railroads, skyscrapers and other capital equipment, increasing each year at a five per cent compound interest rate. But we can use other varieties of capital, especially resource capital, and can probably absorb all our idle workers in providing it. This, however, is not "productive" to the mind of a banker; it is productive only in natural fact. Private bankers will not finance capital improvements of such nature, unless they are guaranteed by the government. If so underwritten, bankers will lend if there are no other outlets for deposits, but grudgingly, disapprovingly. Bankers lend willingly to Empire State Buildings, reluctantly to Norris Dams. If they had their way, most of them would not lend to Norris Dams at all. The financing of resource reconstruction is held to be wasteful, temporary and faintly immoral—like the dole. Proposals for a permanent resource program—like that of the National Resources Board, calling for 105 billion dollars over the next twenty

* For a brief, clear summary see Harold G. Moulton, *The Formation of Capital.* Brookings Institution, 1935.

years—do not register as sound in the minds of most bankers, because they do not produce five per cent golden eggs. Financial traditions are devastated by the suggestion. Where is the money coming from? Better to endure a perpetual army of the idle, a perpetual condition of penury and tightened belts, a desperate and benighted peasantry on failing soil, than to profane the accepted symbols of finance.

Fortunately or unfortunately, perpetual penury is not an alternative, for a financial mechanism geared to expansion will not function on a static basis. It can be stimulated and doped for a short time, but presently it will come to a full stop. The system must change if maturity is a fact. It will change either in the direction of a frozen feudalism with inanimate energy and invention in cold storage, or in the direction of a mechanism which finances public works, reconditions blighted areas, gives work to the idle, permits steady increases in living levels—without choking its values by incrustations of debt.

At this point I am doubtless expected to pull a rabbit out of my hat. I have a hat but no rabbit. Nobody has a rabbit. There are no miracles in finance, despite the career of Charles E. Mitchell. I have a filing case full of detailed plans to revise or revolutionize the financial system, despatched to me by devoted rabbit pullers from all over the nation. Broadly speaking, they are worthless, for the most important consideration of all has been omitted. How are you going to make people *believe* in your system? How is it possible to adjust it to current institutions? The program makers erect a Washington Monument, but neglect the matter of a piece of solid ground on which to put it.

Money in the last analysis is an expression of confidence. When Americans ceased to have confidence in their banks in the early months of 1933, check money evaporated and every bank closed its doors. It may be observed further that confidence cannot be long sustained without a basis of tangible goods and services. One cannot eat money except in those tropic islands where the medium of exchange takes the form of coconuts. If the American people were aware of their economic maturity, and confident that expenditures for restoring the balance of nature were essential and right, there would be no difficulty about the money. It would flow as an expression of that confidence.

There would, however, be some difficulty if labor were scarce and industrial equipment inadequate. Then a choice would have to be made: Shall we use our labor to build up natural resources or to build factories? According to the National Survey of Potential Product Capacity, we have factories enough to give every family in the country almost $5,000 worth of goods and services a year, if they are operated at capacity. We have ten million unemployed, and more coming with every new labor-saving invention. In the adolescent era we made the choice of new factories. They are built, and now no choice remains. A wiser operation of the present industrial plant would certainly absorb some of the unemployed, but not all of them. The only intelligent way to use surplus labor, as we concluded in the last chapter, is in the public-works and -services division.

Businessmen attack the New Deal for actions which they assert destroy confidence. If the allegation were true, we should see a flight from the dollar and swift increases in commodity prices. Real inflation would be under way. This has not happened. There is still ample public confidence in American money, for commodity price movements remain sluggish. The real situation is this. Businessmen have no great confidence in future expansion. The fact of maturity has begun to register in their unconscious minds. Will debts contracted today be met ten years from today with interest at five per cent? Maturity is what really troubles them, not Mr. Roosevelt. Had Mr. Hoover been elected in 1932, the trouble would still be present. Even in 1929 there was no outlet in private plant investment for ten billions of savings, according to the Brookings Institution.

Confidence produces money, especially in an economy of abundance. Let me illustrate this truism. Suppose that President Wilson had proposed an expenditure of twenty-five billion dollars to rehabilitate the slums of American cities in 1917. He would probably have been impeached or committed to an asylum. Only slum dwellers were concerned with their slums; the people as a whole, and the financial community in particular, had no confidence in money put to such use. It would have been, notwithstanding, a fine, human use. President Wilson was forced by circumstances to propose that twenty-five billion dollars be expended for a destructive, inhuman use. He declared war on Germany. The nation, for reasons too complicated to recapitulate, believed in that war, and there was no difficulty about the twenty-five billion dollars. It was not "productive," it was not constructive, it was not even intelligent, but it was validated by public confidence, and one Liberty Loan after another was readily floated.

337

Germany, before Hitler, was bankrupt by all "sound" financial standards. For all I know she is bankrupt today; at least she is not paying her debts. Hitler, again for reasons too complicated to enlarge upon, captured the enthusiasm and confidence of the German people. He proposed a vast program of rearmament—tanks, airplanes, poison gas, pocket battleships, shells, cordite, smokeless powder and other inedible and unwearable commodities. He had no trouble in getting within Germany all the money he desired for this stupendous munitions dump of waste. Observe that there were both unemployment and surplus factory capacity in Germany at the time. The only real difficulty which confronted Hitler was the importing of certain raw materials.

Italy was on the edge of bankruptcy in 1935. Mussolini proposed a war in Ethiopia to cost uncounted lira. Where was the money coming from? The Italian people believed in the war; a quarter of a million troops and mountains of supplies were shipped overseas; the money came again from within the country, and the war was won.

The World War left one-third of France devastated. As in the case of American resources, man, not nature, was responsible. Frenchmen, however, do not devastate their own country; they guard every tree and rivulet. An enemy had perpetrated the damage and the loss must be repaired. The bill ran into astronomical figures. But Frenchmen had confidence in the rightness of the expenditure. One would suppose that after such an exhausting war France would have had no spare cash for rebuilding cathedrals and repairing landscapes. She had plenty of cash because people wanted the work done. Incidentally, these

338

great expenditures for devastated areas kept France from a serious business depression. "In France," says P. J. M. Larrañaga in his *Gold, Glut and Government,** "national reconstruction was not a problem of party politics; it was a unanimous national aspiration. It could not be denied. Besides, it was thought, Germany would pay! France there-fore began her post-war career under the aegis of con-structive government prodigality. . . . It increased the velocity of final buying and of monetary circulation and thereby induced the consequent prodigality among her actively occupied industrial population. To cope with this prodigality, exchange means had to be found by recourse to every method, ancient and modern, orthodox and unorthodox. . . . "

Russia in 1928 had no money and no credit in the Wall Street sense. She proposed to spend thirty billion dollars building dams, factories, railroads and schools. Wall Street rocked with merriment. In 1933 the dams, factories, rail-roads and schools were in place as specified—good, solid structures translated from paper to concrete and steel. Where did Russia get the money? The people believed in the Five Year Plan, even as the French people believed in reconstruction, and as the American people believed in the war. What is believed in passes as gold from hand to hand.

One could continue to cite illustrations indefinitely. Money is confidence. If and when Americans have as much confidence in the rightness of reconditioning their continent as they had in the rightness of war with Germany, there will be no serious trouble about money. This is the only

* George Allen & Unwin, Ltd., 1932.

rabbit I have, but, unless I read the late financial history of France, Germany, Italy, Russia and the United States completely amiss, it is, within its rather severe limitations, a good rabbit, well trained and dependable.

Here and there a banker will be found—I know one or two on Wall Street—who has confidence in public works. The guild as a whole, however, has little or none. The American people follow their bankers, though not so devotedly as before 1929. The concept of infinity has been damaged but not demolished. The fact of maturity has been recognized, but conviction is not universal. Institutions are in flux but have not yet crystallized to new conditions. As in the case of regional planning, another stone wall or two will probably be encountered before we shall believe that dollars spent for saving soil, grass and forest are good dollars. When we do believe it—I think the time is rapidly approaching—we shall have no more trouble about finance than did France in her problem of repairing devastation. I suppose that this is the reason why I am writing this book. I want Americans to *believe* in their grand, broad, beautiful continent.

We must not forget that from the physical point of view public works cost nothing if there is a reserve army of the unemployed who must be fed and sheltered in any event. Cost arises when labor is taken away from some other productive enterprise. Under high energy conditions, other productive enterprises no longer need the labor, for they use kilowatts instead. What a paradox this has created, and how little we realize it. Let me try to make it plain, with the help of Mr. Larrañaga.

PLATE XV.—Transmission tower, Wilson Dam. (*Photo by Charles Krutch.*)

The ruling class under low energy conditions—kings, nobles, generals, clergy—held the mass of the people at subsistence levels and took the surplus. It was not much, but it furnished courts, cathedrals and a military establishment. So far as possible the mass was encouraged to work harder. Produce, you lazy villeins! Under high energy conditions we find an amazing reversal. The ruling group—now corporate administrators—in effect command the mass to work less. Workers are discharged or put on part time. The idea is to restrict production, keep the surplus down, lest it ruin prices. Quit work, you villeins!

The revolt of the masses in scarcity societies was aimed at keeping more of the meager surplus, at dividing up. The revolt in abundance societies must be aimed at barred factory doors. Open them and let us go to work. Give us opportunity to produce on any front. The corporate administrators have no grudge against high living standards as such. A few congenital Scrooges would enforce scarcity for the power it gives them, but mostly factory doors are locked because administrators are afraid of loss. If an adequate financial demand were in sight, they would be delighted to operate at capacity. Demand fails, and the knee-jerk response on the part of the tycoons is to restrict production.

The condition becomes increasingly fantastic, especially with the decline of growth curves in population and the other evidences of maturity. The state enters as a third party in an attempt to resolve the deadlock. It opens opportunities in public works to give jobs and purchasing power to the locked-out laborers. States all over the world are doing precisely this on a huge scale. America is doing it to the tune

341

of some three billions a year. The difficulty in the United States is that the money, being largely borrowed from private bankers, is added to the public debt. In the end, I see no other course than to allow the state to be its own banker, to issue its own money and credit on substantially a non-interest-bearing basis and to employ the income tax to shift savings to reconstruction. Such a program will keep debt at negotiable proportions, put public works on a permanent basis, with especial reference to resource planning, and absorb every able-bodied individual, every young graduate, who cannot secure occupation in other enterprises. By increasing living standards it will gradually unlock factory doors.

Frankly, does this not make sense? When enough citizens believe that it does, it can be done. Unemployment will fade into the nightmare of a barbarous past, where men were beginning to live in abundance conditions while still thinking in terms of scarcity. It is your belief which must govern. This is the way human institutions work.

History Lesson

Saint Paul preached in the city of Antioch, thundering against its pride of wealth and its sins. There were 400,000 people in the city; the pleasure gardens of Daphne were famous throughout the Mediterranean world. Today it is a miserable dusty Syrian town of 30,000. Archeologists reconstruct its ancient grandeur after digging through eighteen feet of detritus. Antioch perished not from its sins but from erosion on the Taurus and Lebanon Rivers. Protective terraces were neglected, forests were cut off, and the silt

342

and gravel streamed down, as it streams from Ducktown today. "There is after all," says *Fortune*, "no philosophical difference between the fate of Antioch in Syria and the possible fate of Garden City in Kansas." There is, however, a decided mechanical difference. The simple Syrian plowed four roods in a day; the simple Kansan plows 117. The machine has enabled us to telescope the old pattern.

Suppose we take a rapid swing about the world's continents. South America, according to Harry Slattery of the Department of the Interior, has held its soil reasonably well. The ancient Incas built on the slopes of the Andes the most stupendous system of terraces ever engineered. Spanish conquerors were hard on native peoples but not so hard on the land. They respected the balance of nature. When soil experts in the United States were voices crying in the wilderness twenty years ago, Argentina listened. She imported a brigade of them, and today has a magnificent range control on the pampas, government enforced. There will be no Dust Bowl in the Argentine.

The Maya built a great civilization in Central America and Mexico. Their agricultural pattern called for cutting the jungle, burning it and growing corn until the soil was depleted. Then—touched with the concept of infinity—they moved on to a new patch of jungle. After a hundred years or so fields were so distant from the cities that farmers returned to the old fields, hoping that the jungle might have restored the soil. But nature does not work quite so rapidly even in the tropics. The cities were left without the means of life and had to be deserted. New cities were established,

343

but ultimately the land ran out. The great Maya culture was already far gone in decay when Cortes landed in Yucatan.

The North African coast was once a famous wine region. Now, over great areas, the desert creeps in. East Africa is going the way of the Great Plains, except where the tsetse fly acts as range marshal. The Union of South Africa has been hard hit, but the warning has been heeded. A soil-saving program has been inaugurated, with the government paying seven-eighths of the cost.

In January, 1936, 300,000 tons of red dust fell over Victoria. Australia has a natural desert in her central portions, but overgrazing and the plague of imported rabbits are widening the area. "Weather Bureau officials admit that the dust storms may be regarded as a warning that the soil is being denuded, and that remedial measures must be taken to preserve it with binding vegetation."

Japan began systematic erosion control fifty years ago. The government pays five-sixths of the cost and compels the cooperation of property owners.

India and China are both dependent upon water from the Himalayas. The soil bookkeeping of India shows a chronic deficit. In 1770 ten million people died of famine. The margin of subsistence is slim. Not only water but soil comes down from Tibet. This is natural wash, for the upland natives neither strip forests nor subject grasslands to an excess of cattle. Without this present from the hills of another country, the population of India could not be supported. The Dekkan peninsula has lost its forests and erosion, as reported by Sears, is widespread. We have already noted how man-made deserts have formed east of tne Caspian in Asia and how Russia is waging war upon them.

China presents us with both a horrible warning and examples of more or less desperate control. Dr. W. C. Lowdermilk of the Soil Conservation Service has spent five years in China studying its agriculture, forests and erosion problems. In 1877 a flood on the Yellow River drowned one million people. He reports that it is too late for dams as flood-control measures; silt washing down from upland hills and plateaus would quickly fill them. These hills have been denuded of forest and overgrazing has torn off the grass cover. Dust storms are common. Some control has been started in the headwaters—the only possible solution with large engineering works out of the picture—but the war with Japan has checked the work. Dr. Lowdermilk has looked into gullies 600 feet deep, three times as bad as Stewart County. As the soil goes into the Yellow Sea, China is being forced to narrower acreage and her standards of living fall. She has no more arable land for 400 millions of people than the United States has for 130 millions—but 85 per cent of all Chinese labor is devoted to growing food. Good soil, where it is being held, is the result of unbelievable exertion, terracing, irrigation works, fertilizing and even the application of "night soil," human excreta. Once China respected the balance of nature, but recent increases in lumbering and cattle grazing have broken it.

Some students, such as Ellsworth Huntington, believe that China is turning to desert in many areas because the climate is changing. Dr. Lowdermilk disputes this, and bases his opinion on the "temple forests." As he went about the desert country, he encountered monasteries set in small thriving forests. Natural deserts do not support forests. All the land here was once wooded and green and pleasant. It would still be green and pleasant if most of the trees had not been cut down. Buddhist monks require woods in which to walk and meditate, and their woods were spared. The desert is thus man-made, and the temple forests provide a beautiful controlled experiment to prove it.

We cross from Asia to Europe. Greek farmers at the time of the siege of Troy were sturdy yeomen. In due time, owner-operator gave way to tenant, slave and absentee owner. Landlords mined the soil for quick profit. Holdings gained in size. Ultimately Athens became dependent on the grain of the black earth of Russia, beyond the Dardanelles. When her enemies closed the straits, Greek civilization ended. Forests were slashed from the hills and Greece became drier. I once wandered over the hills of Greece and looked in vain for my schoolbook glories. Barren, dry and desolate they were. The Vale of Delphi seemed an oasis in a desert.

Much the same pattern can be traced in Rome. Yeomen and strength; then tenantry, slavery, latifundia, soil depletion. Augustus saw the danger. Horace and Virgil praised bucolic virtues in deathless verse, while Rome was fed by fleets of wallowing galleys from North Africa. Her rich lands turned to poor lands. The Roman Empire became an interesting item to place upon the dusty shelf of history.

When iron and steel manufacturing became general in western Europe after the middle ages, forests were mercilessly leveled to obtain charcoal for the smelters.

Feudal lords shifted from fief to fief as their lands wore out, like the Maya. Church property however was well managed.

The continent of Europe began to degenerate physically. Its bookkeeping with nature was askew. The Renaissance helped to arouse men to the situation. Crop rotation was introduced and the planting of legumes, though their nitrogen-fixing function had not been discovered. The Flemish and Dutch developed valuable soil techniques in the low countries. The Royal Society of London under Charles II began to study the Great Wheel. Pasteur discovered bacteria and opened up new soil knowledge. Testy old Baron von Liebig began his indomitable search for the perfect fertilizer. Scandinavia put forests on a permanent-yield basis. The degeneration was halted, although Europe is still unable to feed herself and must import food.

The National Resources Board recently dispatched an expert to inquire into resource planning in England, Germany, Austria, Switzerland, Italy, Czechoslovakia and France. He reported that all these countries had more or less complete government control of water resources, that all had highly developed forestry departments, that all exercised rigid supervision over pollution, that drainage and irrigation projects were carefully planned, that hydro-electric plants were either owned or effectively controlled by government and—we might add—that private companies did not run whimpering to Supreme Courts. The Rhone Valley Authority in France, controlling irrigation, navigation and power in the whole basin, is a European version of the TVA.

347

German forests have long been supervised by the Reich with an aggressive policy of reforestation and protection. Cutting on private lands may be stopped if not properly done. All private waste lands not suitable for crops must be planted to forest if so required. Czechoslovakia works on a National Power Plan. The country is divided into twenty districts, with a limited dividend corporation in each district. Sixty per cent of the stock is owned by public bodies, forty per cent by private capital. Under the plan, "the whole country is being systematically electrified." In Austria drainage works receive a government subsidy and are strictly administered as to function. Provincial governments grant concessions for flood control. Municipalities and towns supervise little waters. England is divided into forty-eight drainage areas, administered by "Catchment Boards"—charming title. The Thames Conservancy is centuries old. It directs the functions of the whole drainage basin above London, with splendid pollution protection on even the smallest tributaries. England has no serious erosion problems because rains are gentle and because she has kept sod on the slopes.

The first national forest law was enacted in Sweden in 1600. Half of the country is timbered, the largest supply in Europe except for Russia. Land was classified by a land-use survey in 1752. We are just beginning to think about such a survey, almost 200 years later. The Swedish government owns eleven million acres of forest and administers in addition two million acres of municipal forest and 750,000 acres of state church forest. After cutting, the private owner is required to reforest at once. No more private forest lands can be purchased, so government lands grow steadily. The state as lumberman competes on equal terms, paying full taxes. Profits to the government in 1928 were $4,300,000. Private lumber companies are administered by trained foresters—they have to be so administered to keep up with expert government practice. Our lumber barons looked on foresters as a pugilist looks at a bookkeeper.

Ditches are dug, brooks cleared, sites inspected, pine and spruce seedlings set out. Annual cut is matched with annual growth, and the trees of Sweden do not decline. There are fifty-five state forestry schools.

Woodcraft is passed from father to son. In the winters when fields are covered with snow, many farmers work in the state woods, particularly in those regions where poor soils do not yield adequate income from crops alone. The workers bring their own horses and operate on piece rates. Year after year they report in the same area, giving a permanent and stable labor supply for skilled foresters to direct. Saw mills go on cutting forever. The valley about them is never denuded. Such a town as Jewsöbaden is an enduring community, comfortable, prosperous, and a model of cleanliness.*

Western Europe plans with nature, so far as national boundaries and bisecting watersheds permit. But in other parts of Europe, in large areas in Africa, in India, in China and now in Australia, the opposite has been true. Soils have been ravaged at a rate beyond the capacity of nature to repair. Civilization after civilization in the past has been reared on borrowed capital, and the security was the good

* Marquis W. Childs: *Sweden, the Middle Way.*

earth, not bankers' paper. Mesopotamia, Egypt, North Africa, Greece, Rome and Mexico under the Maya worked through their resource assets and passed into limbo.

"The lone and level sands stretch far away. . . . "

The Great Wheel turns. A continent is *situs*, a place to live, and so far more than a bread factory. People do not make continents; continents make a people. The age-long strength of Russia is due to her latitude, climate, resources and sweep. The strength of England is due to her position in the sea. The strength of our nation is due to the continent of North America. It has molded us, nourished us, fed its abundant vitality into our veins. We are its children, lost and homeless without its strong arms about us. Shall we destroy it?

SELECTED BIBLIOGRAPHY

GOVERNMENT

Little Waters, by H. S. Person, with the cooperation of E. Johnston Coil and Robert T. Beall. 82 pages. U. S. Government Printing Office, 1935.

General Report of the National Resources Board, Dec. 1, 1934. 455 pages. U. S. Government Printing Office.

Report of the Mississippi Valley Committee, Oct. 1, 1934. 2 volumes. U. S. Government Printing Office.

Regional Factors in National Planning and Development. National Resources Committee, December 1935. 223 pages. U. S. Government Printing Office.

State Planning. National Resources Committee, September 1935. 310 pages. U. S. Government Printing Office.

Report on Water Pollution. National Resources Committee, July 1935. 82 pages. Multigraphed.

Plan for New England. National Resources Committee, June 1935. Multigraphed.

Floods in the United States, Magnitude and Frequency, by C. S. Jarvis and others. Geological Survey Water Supply Paper 771. 497 pages. U. S. Government Printing Office, 1936.

Rainfall and Runoff in the United States. Geological Survey Water Supply Paper 772. 301 pages. U. S. Government Printing Office, 1936.

Conservation in the Department of the Interior, by Ray Lyman Wilbur and William Atherton DuPuy. 253 pages. U. S. Government Printing Office, 1932.

Annual reports of Forest Service, Soil Conservation Service, Biological Survey, Resettlement Administration, Civilian Conservation Corps, Department of the Interior.

A Study of Wisconsin, Its Resources, Its Physical, Social and Economic Background. 501 pages. Wisconsin Regional Planning Committee, Madison. 1934.

Forest Land Use in Wisconsin. Report of Committee on Land Use and Forestry, April, 1932. 156 pages. State Capitol, Madison.

GENERAL

PAUL B. SEARS: *Deserts on the March*. University of Oklahoma Press, 1935.

VAN HISE AND HAVEMEYER: *Conservation of Our Natural Resources*. The Macmillan Company, 1935.

351

E. W. ZIMMERMAN: *World Resources and Industries*. Harper & Brothers, 1933.

A. B. HULBERT: *Soil, Its Influence on the History of the United States*. Yale University Press, 1930.

ROBERT MARSHALL: *The People's Forest*. Harrison Smith & Robert Haas, Inc., 1933.

OVID BUTLER, editor: *American Conservation*. American Forestry Association. 1935.

Recent Social Trends in the United States. McGraw-Hill Book Company, Inc., 1933.

J. RUSSELL SMITH: *North America*. Harcourt, Brace & Company, 1925.

J. A. POMFRET: *The Geographical Pattern of Mankind*. D. Appleton-Century Company, Inc., 1935.

M. ILIN: *Men and Mountains*. J. B. Lippincott Company, 1935.

BROOKS EMENY: *The Strategy of Raw Materials*. The Macmillan Company, 1934.

J. F. HORRABIN: *An Outline of Economic Geography*. The Plebs League, London, 1924.

G. D. H. COLE: *Economic Planning*. Alfred A. Knopf, Inc., 1935.

JOHNSON, EMBREE and ALEXANDER: *The Collapse of Cotton Tenancy*. University of North Carolina Press, 1935.

MARQUIS W. CHILDS: *Sweden, the Middle Way*. Yale University Press, 1936.

H. B. HAWES: *Fish and Game, Now or Never*. D. Appleton-Century Company, Inc., 1935.

HAROLD L. ICKES: *Back to Work*. The Macmillan Company, 1935.

JESNERS and NOWELL: *A Program for Land Use in Northern Minnesota*. University of Minnesota Press, 1935.

BENTON MACKAYE: *The New Exploration*. Harcourt, Brace & Company, 1928.

Fortune Magazine: The Grasslands, November, 1935.

J. W. BEWS: *Human Ecology*. Oxford University Press, 1935.

Index

E

Eastern Plateau, the, 11
Ecology, 55, 62–65
Egypt, 154
Emeny, Brooks, 196
England (*see* Great Britain)
Ericsson, Lief, 26
Euphrates River, 17, 243
Everglades, the, 11

F

Farm Credit Authority, 217
Federal Bureau of Fisheries, 184
Federal Emergency Relief Administration (FERA), 173
Federal Power Commission, 248, 303
Federal Reserve System, 248, 295
Federal Trade Commission, 248
Fergusson, Erna, 110*n*
Ferris, John P., 289
Fertilizer, 58, 89, 90, 211–214
Finley, William, 44
Fisheries, 43, 184, 185
Floods, 22, 23, 41, 168–175
Florida, 8, 11, 26, 145, 212, 225, 226, 326
Flyways, 185–189
Ford, Henry, 55, 158, 232
Forest Service, the, 88, 119–121, 125, 126, 131, 132, 247, 249, 277, 298, 306, 312–314, 327
Fortune Magazine, 45*n*, 110, 113
France, 123, 197, 198, 222, 228, 338, 339, 347
Free market, 244, 245
Furnas, C. C., 59, 179

G

Ganges River, 17
Gartner, Prof. Ross A., 196
Geological Survey, the, 250, 277, 297, 306
Georgia, 6, 8, 11, 49, 88, 156, 264, 266, 309
Gericke, Dr. W. F., 58
Germany, 120, 152, 197, 198, 201, 211, 222, 289, 338, 339, 347, 348
Grainger County, Tenn., 235*ff.*, 263, 267, 292, 293, 327
Grand Canyon of the Colorado, 9, 83, 175
Gray, L. C., 261
Great Basin, 9, 12, 14, 15, 27, 172, 217
Great Britain, 20, 46, 163, 164, 195–198, 200, 201, 206–208, 289, 347, 348, 350
Great Lakes, 8, 11, 16, 28, 72, 148, 182, 217
Great Lakes Plains, 11
Great Plains, 12, 14, 15, 27, 38, 41, 100*ff.*, 172, 173, 178, 189, 216, 222, 300, 331
Great Salt Lake, 9, 12, 35, 151, 180
Great Slave Lake, 28
Great Smoky Mountains, 28, 49, 213, 326
Great Swamp region of Wisconsin, 144–145
Great Wheel, the, 69*ff.*, 82, 140, 162, 174, 190, 214, 253, 254, 294, 298, 347, 350
Greenland, 29
Gulf of Mexico, 6, 15, 38, 169, 170

355

Date Due

APR 18 '5?		
FEB 7 '57		
APR 16 '58		
5-28		
APR 17 67 pd		
NOV 21 '68		
DEC 2 '68		
FEB 6 1969		
MAY 8 1979		
APR 12 '87		